MESSIAH

Illustrations by Jeff Anderson
Text by Mike Maddox

This edition copyright © 2000 Lion Publishing
Text copyright © 1998 Mike Maddox
Illustrations copyright © 1998 Jeff Anderson
Lettering copyright © 1998 Steve Harrison

The moral rights of the author,
illustrator and letterer have been asserted

Published by
Lion Publishing plc
Sandy Lane West, Oxford, England
www.lion-publishing.co.uk
ISBN 0 7459 4419 1

First published as part of the
Lion Graphic Bible in 1998
Messiah first published 2000
10 9 8 7 6 5 4 3 2 1 0

Printed and bound in Belgium

A LION BOOK

IN THE BEGINNING WAS THE **WORD**, AND THE WORD WAS WITH **GOD**, AND THE WORD **WAS** GOD...

ALL THINGS CAME INTO BEING THROUGH **HIM**, AND WITHOUT HIM NOT ONE THING CAME INTO BEING.

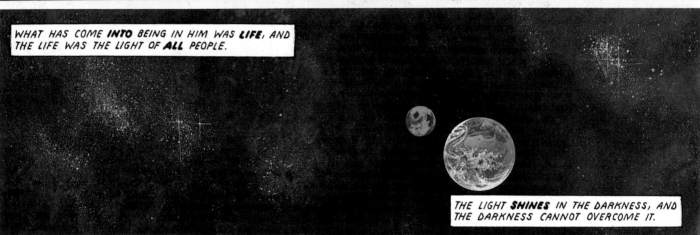

WHAT HAS COME **INTO** BEING IN HIM WAS **LIFE**, AND THE LIFE WAS THE LIGHT OF **ALL** PEOPLE.

THE LIGHT **SHINES** IN THE DARKNESS, AND THE DARKNESS CANNOT OVERCOME IT.

THERE WAS A MAN CALLED **JOHN**. HE HIMSELF WAS NOT THE LIGHT, BUT CAME AS A **WITNESS** TO THE LIGHT, THAT ALL MIGHT BELIEVE.

THE **TRUE** LIGHT, WHICH ENLIGHTENS EVERYONE WAS COMING INTO THE **WORLD**!

AND SO GOD STARTS TO UNFOLD THE NEXT STAGE OF HIS GREAT PLAN, DRAWING TOGETHER THE THREADS SET IN PLACE SINCE THE DAWN OF TIME.

AND, AS ALWAYS WITH GOD, IT BEGINS, NOT WITH KINGS AND QUEENS AND GENERALS, BUT WITH ORDINARY MEN AND WOMEN LIVING ORDINARY LIVES...

4

WHICH BRINGS US TO NAZARETH, A TOWN IN THE HILL-COUNTRY OF GALILEE, IN THE NORTH OF ISRAEL.

MARY, A YOUNG WOMAN, IS ENGAGED TO BE MARRIED TO JOSEPH, A LOCAL CARPENTER.

UNDER ROMAN OCCUPATION, ISRAEL IS RULED BY A PUPPET KING, CORRUPT, AND DIVORCED FROM THE PEOPLE.

BUT JOSEPH IS A DESCENDANT OF KING DAVID, IN A LINE THAT STRETCHES BACK TO ABRAHAM.

HERE, THROUGH THE LIVES OF ORDINARY PEOPLE, AMIDST THE UNREMARKABLE AND THE MUNDANE, GOD FINALLY BRINGS HIS PLAN TO FRUITION.

SOMETHING **WONDERFUL** IS ABOUT TO HAPPEN...

REJOICE, MARY, FOR GOD IS WITH YOU! BLESSED ARE YOU AMONG WOMEN! OF ALL THE WOMEN ON EARTH, YOU HAVE FOUND FAVOUR WITH GOD!

BE AT PEACE, AND HAVE NO FEAR!

ME? BUT I DON'T UNDERSTAND - I MEAN, I'M NO ONE SPECIAL. WHAT HAVE I DONE?

YOU WILL HAVE A CHILD, AND HIS NAME WILL BE JESUS!

HE WILL BE CALLED THE SON OF THE MOST HIGH. THE LORD GOD HIMSELF WILL GIVE HIM THE THRONE OF HIS ANCESTOR, DAVID. HE WILL RULE THE DESCENDANTS OF THE HOUSE OF JACOB FOR EVER!

AND OF HIS KINGDOM, THERE WILL BE NO END!

BUT HOW? I'M NOT PREGNANT; I'M NOT EVEN MARRIED, I-I'M STILL A VIRGIN!

THE HOLY SPIRIT WILL REST UPON YOU, AND THE POWER OF GOD WILL OVERSHADOW YOU. IN THIS WAY YOUR CHILD WILL BE CALLED THE SON OF GOD.

NOTHING IS IMPOSSIBLE TO GOD! YOUR OWN RELATIVE, ELIZABETH - CHILDLESS AND PAST CHILD-BEARING - IS NOW SIX MONTHS PREGNANT. NOTHING IS IMPOSSIBLE, MARY! NOTHING!

STIRRED BY THE ANGEL'S WORDS, MARY MADE HER WAY SOUTH TO THE HILLS OF JUDEA, TO VISIT HER COUSIN ELIZABETH. PERHAPS SHE COULD ANSWER SOME OF MARY'S QUESTIONS.

BUT ELIZABETH'S GREETING TOOK HER ABACK...

MARY! GOD'S BLESSING IS ON YOU ABOVE ALL WOMEN ON EARTH, AND BLESSED IS THE CHILD YOU WILL BEAR!

AS SOON AS I HEARD YOUR VOICE, THE CHILD IN MY WOMB LEAPED FOR JOY!!

MY SPIRIT AND MY SOUL REJOICE IN GOD. FROM THIS DAY ON, ALL PEOPLE WILL COUNT ME HAPPY, BECAUSE OF WHAT GOD HAS DONE. HE HAS KEPT HIS PROMISE TO COME TO HIS PEOPLE'S AID.

MARY STAYED THREE MONTHS WITH [H]ER COUSIN, AND THEN RETURNED HOME[.]

IN TIME, ELIZABETH GAVE BIRTH TO A BOY, AS THE ANGEL HAD PREDICTED.

HE'S BEAUTIFUL, ELIZABETH. YOU MUST BE SO HAPPY. YOU'LL NAME HIM ZECHARIAH, AFTER HIS FATHER?

INDEED, THAT'S TO BE EXPECTED - AND HE CERTAINLY HAS HIS FATHER'S EYES!

THE CHILD IS GOD'S SPECIAL GIFT TO US - AND WE'RE GOING TO CALL HIM JOHN.

AREN'T WE, DEAR?

JOHN.

ZECHARIAH MADE HIS AGREEMENT CLEAR - AND WITH THAT, HE BEGAN TO SPEAK AGAIN!

BUT WHILE ELIZABETH AND ZECHARIAH REJOICED IN THEIR GOOD FORTUNE, IN THE TOWN OF NAZARETH, THINGS WERE NOT GOING SO SMOOTHLY...

JOSEPH! WHY ARE YOU STILL WORKING AT THIS HOUR? COME OUT, MAN, YOU CAN'T HIDE IN HERE FOR EVER!

I'M NOT HIDING! I HAVE NOTHING **TO** HIDE!

I JUST WANTED TO GET THE JOB FINISHED ON TIME, THAT'S ALL. WHY? WHAT ARE PEOPLE SAYING?

THOUGH I CAN WORK THAT OUT FOR MYSELF. THERE'S NO HIDING IT NOW, IS THERE? SHE GETS LARGER EACH DAY.

WHAT CAN BE DONE, JOSEPH? IT'S NOT AS IF YOU'RE THE FIRST TO MARRY IN A HURRY!

TRUE. BUT I KNOW FOR A FACT THE CHILD ISN'T MINE. AND THAT KNOWLEDGE IS KILLING ME..!

UNDER JEWISH LAW AN ENGAGEMENT WAS AS BINDING AS MARRIAGE, AND JOSEPH COULD HAVE PUBLICLY HUMILIATED MARY, EVEN ACCUSING HER OF ADULTERY!

BUT JOSEPH WAS A GOOD MAN. SO INSTEAD, HE DECIDED TO BREAK THE CONTRACT PRIVATELY. A QUIET DIVORCE SEEMED BEST.

ONLY THEN, AFTER THE DECISION WHICH SHOWED HIS GENTLENESS, DID GOD LET JOSEPH IN ON HIS PLAN. AN ANGEL CAME TO JOSEPH IN HIS SLEEP...

GREETINGS JOSEPH, SON OF DAVID. DO NOT BE AFRAID TO TAKE MARY AS YOUR WIFE.

BUT SHE IS ALREADY PREGNANT!

- AND SHE WILL HAVE A SON. YOU WILL CALL HIM *JESUS*, FOR HE WILL SAVE HIS PEOPLE FROM THEIR SINS. IT IS THROUGH THE HOLY SPIRIT THAT MARY HAS CONCEIVED.

DO NOT BE AFRAID TO TAKE HER AS YOUR WIFE, SON OF DAVID.

THE PROPHET ISAIAH, HUNDREDS OF YEARS BEFORE HAD SAID THAT A VIRGIN WOULD BEAR A CHILD, WHO WOULD BE CALLED *IMMANUEL*. 'GOD WITH US'.

AND AS THE ANGEL LEFT, JOSEPH KNEW THESE WORDS TO BE TRUE.

AND SO HE MARRIED MARY.

THEIRS WASN'T THE FIRST WEDDING WHERE THE BRIDE WAS OBVIOUSLY PREGNANT, NOR WAS IT THE LAST. BUT JOSEPH TRUSTED THE WORDS OF THE ANGEL, AND TURNED A DEAF EAR TO THE GOSSIP-MONGERS.

JOSEPH TOOK MARY HOME, BUT HE DID NOT SLEEP WITH HIS WIFE UNTIL AFTER HER SON WAS BORN.

THEY BOTH KNEW THAT THIS CHILD WAS SPECIAL...

IN THOSE DAYS, THE ROMAN EMPEROR CAESAR AUGUSTUS ISSUED A DECREE: A CENSUS WAS TO BE TAKEN THROUGHOUT THE EMPIRE, EACH PERSON GOING TO HIS HOME TOWN TO BE REGISTERED.

AND SO JOSEPH TOOK HIS YOUNG WIFE, AND TOGETHER THEY MADE THEIR WAY SOUTH TO THE PLACE WHERE JOSEPH MUST REGISTER; THE TOWN WHERE RUTH HAD MARRIED BOAZ, THE BIRTHPLACE OF KING DAVID...

THE TOWN OF *BETHLEHEM*.

ISRAEL BRISTLED WITH ANGER, RIPE FOR REBELLION UNDER ROMAN RULE.

MANY WAITED FOR THE MESSIAH WHO WOULD RESCUE THEM, RESTORE THEIR FORTUNES, DRIVE THE ROMANS FROM THE LAND.

IT WAS AGAINST THIS BACKGROUND THAT MARY AND JOSEPH LIVED THEIR LIVES.

PLEASE! WE DESPERATELY NEED A ROOM. WE'VE TRIED EVERYWHERE...

SORRY SIR, WE'RE FULLY BOOKED, HAVE BEEN FOR WEEKS. HERE FOR THE CENSUS, ARE WE? WELL, DON'T BLAME ME, BLAME THE ROMANS! IT'S THEIR IDEA!

PLEASE — MY WIFE... THE BABY'S DUE ANY DAY NOW. THERE MUST BE **SOMEWHERE** WE COULD STAY.

IT'S NOT MUCH, I KNOW, BUT IT'S WARM AND DRY, AND MORE TO THE POINT, IT'S ALL I HAVE LEFT.

WE'LL TAKE IT.

WE'LL TAKE IT, JOSEPH! I DON'T THINK I CAN WAIT MUCH LONGER! THE BABY'S COMING!

BUT SURELY THERE MUST BE —

WE'LL TAKE IT!

800 YEARS BEFORE, THE PROPHET MICAH WROTE THESE WORDS: 'FROM YOU, BETHLEHEM, SMALL AS YOU ARE, WILL COME A RULER FOR ISRAEL, WHOSE FAMILY LINE GOES BACK TO ANCIENT TIMES. HE WILL RULE WITH THE STRENGTH THAT COMES FROM GOD... AND HE WILL BRING PEACE.'

THE SON OF GOD. THE NEW ADAM. KING OF KINGS AND LORD OF LORDS.

HE CAME INTO THE WORLD A HELPLESS BABY, BORN IN A CATTLE-SHED.

TONIGHT, THOSE WORDS WOULD COME TRUE. THE GREATEST KING THE WORLD WOULD EVER SEE, COME AT LAST FOR A PEOPLE WHO HAD CRIED OUT FOR HIM FOR CENTURIES.

BUT NOT IN TRIUMPH AT THE HEAD OF A MIGHTY ARMY, BANNERS IN THE WIND, SHIELDS HELD HIGH.

IN THE HILLS ABOVE THE TOWN, A GROUP OF SHEPHERDS WATCHED OVER THEIR SHEEP AS THEIR FOREFATHERS HAD DONE FOR GENERATIONS.

AND AS THEY SAT AROUND THEIR CAMPFIRE THAT NIGHT, THE MOST AMAZING THING HAPPENED...

AN ANGEL OF THE LORD APPEARED, AND GOD'S GLORY SHONE ABOUT THEM. THEY WERE TERRIFIED! BUT THE ANGEL SAID —

DO NOT BE AFRAID! I BRING WONDERFUL NEWS! TODAY IN THE TOWN OF DAVID YOUR SAVIOUR IS BORN: CHRIST, THE MESSIAH! YOU WILL FIND A BABY WRAPPED IN CLOTHS AND LYING IN A MANGER. THEN YOU WILL KNOW!

AND SUDDENLY A GREAT COMPANY OF THE ANGELS OF HEAVEN APPEARED, SINGING PRAISE TO GOD:

GLORY TO GOD IN THE HIGHEST HEAVEN! AND PEACE ON EARTH TO ALL WHO PLEASE HIM.

BUT THE WONDERS SURROUNDING THE CHILD'S BIRTH WERE FAR FROM OVER, FOR WHEN THEY TOOK THE CHILD TO THE TEMPLE, AS WAS THE JEWISH CUSTOM...

ONE DAY, AS EVENING FELL, A GROUP OF IMPORTANT TRAVELLERS FROM THE EAST ARRIVED AT THE PALACE OF HEROD, THE KING.

ALTHOUGH WEARY FROM THEIR JOURNEY, THEIR GAZE STILL HELD TO THE SKIES, WHERE THE FIRST STARS OF TWILIGHT SHOWED...

GREETINGS. WE HAVE TRAVELLED FROM FAR IN THE EAST, SEEKING THE KING OF THE JEWS.

AND YOU HAVE FOUND M! I AM HEROD, NG OF ISRAEL.

THEN I FEAR THAT WE HAVE MADE A GRAVE ERROR. WE ARE ASTRONOMERS, OUR LIFE'S WORK THE STUDY OF THE STARS ABOVE.

WE WITNESSED A NEW STAR, A THING **UNHEARD** OF IN OUR OWN TIME. IT LEADS US HERE, TO WHERE THE KING OF THE JEWS IS TO BE BORN AT THIS TIME.

... PERHAPS IT MEANS YOUR SON? IS YOUR WIFE EXPECTING?

HEROD KNEW THAT THE PROPHETS HAD NAMED BETHLEHEM AS THE BIRTHPLACE OF THE MESSIAH, SO HE DIRECTED THEM THERE.

MAKE A CAREFUL SEARCH FOR THE CHILD. AND WHEN YOU FIND HIM ... **TELL** ME WON'T YOU? SO I MAY WORSHIP HIM TOO?

HEROD HAD KEPT POWER UNDER THE ROMANS BY GUILE AND CUNNING, BUT THE STRAIN HAD LEFT HIM DEEPLY PARANOID.

SO HE MADE PLANS TO KILL THE CHILD, IN ORDER TO PRESERVE HIS OWN THRONE.

GOD HAD SPOKEN TO ORDINARY PEOPLE – THROUGH DREAMS, THROUGH ANGELS, THROUGH THE SCRIPTURES – TO ANNOUNCE THE GREAT EVENT.

NOW, AS THE WISE MEN FOLLOWED THE STAR TOWARDS BETHLEHEM, NATURE ITSELF BESPOKE THE CHILD'S BIRTH!

THE WISE MEN FOLLOWED THE STAR, UNTIL IT RESTED OVER THE PLACE WHERE THE CHILD LAY SLEEPING.

THE KING OF THE JEWS – FOUND NOT IN A PALACE OR CASTLE, BUT IN AN ORDINARY HOUSE, IN THE CARE OF ORDINARY WORKING PEOPLE...

WHO'S THAT AT THE DOOR AT THIS HOUR?

I HAVEN'T ASKED ANYONE TO CALL. I WAS ABOUT TO BATHE THE BABY. SEE WHO IT IS, WOULD YOU?

MARY? YOU'RE NEVER GOING TO BELIEVE THIS!

GREETINGS! WE COME LOOKING FOR THE KING OF THE JEWS.

10

THE WISE MEN DID NOT HESITATE. THEY CAME INTO THIS PLAIN HOUSE BEARING GIFTS FIT FOR A KING — GOLD, INCENSE AND MYRRH.

THEY SAW THE CHILD THEY HAD TRAVELLED SO FAR TO SEE.

AND THEY **WORSHIPPED** HIM.

BE WARNED, JOSEPH. WE HAVE DREAMT OF HEROD, AND DO NOT TRUST HIM! HE EXPECTS US AT HIS PALACE TO BRING NEWS OF... YOUR SON, SHALL WE SAY?

WE INTEND TO RETURN HOME THE LONG WAY, TO AVOID HIM AT ALL COSTS. TAKE CARE, JOSEPH!

THAT NIGHT, JOSEPH HAD A TERRIBLE DREAM. HE MUST TAKE MARY AND JESUS AND LEAVE AT ONCE FOR EGYPT. JOSEPH HAD SEEN SO MUCH THAT HE KNEW THE WARNING WAS NOT TO BE TAKEN LIGHTLY.

THEY CAME AT DAWN.

THIS WAY! I HEARD CRYING!

THIS ONE'S A BOY! KILL IT!

PLEASE! HE'S ONLY A CHILD! HOW CAN YOU DO THIS?

SHUT YOUR MOUTH OR **JOIN** HIM!

EVERY MALE CHILD UNDER TWO YEARS OLD.

THEIR MOTHERS SCREAMED, AND REFUSED TO BE COMFORTED, BUT THERE WAS NOTHING ANYONE COULD DO TO STOP THEM.

IN HIS JEALOUSY, HEROD MURDERED THE INNOCENT TO PROTECT HIS THRONE. WITHIN A YEAR HE HIMSELF WAS DEAD.

AFTER HEROD'S DEATH, AN ANGEL SPOKE IN A DREAM TO JOSEPH. IT WAS SAFE TO GO HOME.

SO JOSEPH TOOK HIS FAMILY, AND RETURNED. NOT TO BETHLEHEM, BUT TO GALILEE, TO THE TOWN OF **NAZARETH**.

EVERY YEAR, MARY AND JOSEPH WENT SOUTH TO JERUSALEM TO CELEBRATE THE PASSOVER. THERE WERE A GREAT MANY PEOPLE ON THE ROADS AT THAT TIME, AND WHOLE COMMUNITIES MIGHT TRAVEL TOGETHER TO WORSHIP GOD.

JESUS WAS NOW TWELVE YEARS OLD.

JOSEPH — HAVE YOU SEEN JESUS? I THOUGHT HE WAS TRAVELLING WITH **BOAZ'S** FAMILY, BUT THEY HAVEN'T SEEN HIM!

BOAZ ?! I THOUGHT HE WAS TRAVELLING WITH **SIMEON'S** FAMILY! I'VE A BAD FEELING ABOUT THIS! I THINK HE'S STILL IN **JERUSALEM** !

I **KNEW** WE SHOULDN'T HAVE LET HIM OUT OF OUR SIGHT !

THE SEARCH TOOK THEM **THREE DAYS**. SICK WITH WORRY, THEY EVENTUALLY THOUGHT TO LOOK IN THE **TEMPLE** ITSELF. AND IT WAS THERE, AMONG THE WISEST MEN IN ISRAEL, THAT THEY WERE TO FIND HIM...

SO WHAT DO YOU THINK THAT MEANS ?

...!?

WELL, IT'S...

JESUS, WHAT ARE YOU **DOING** HERE ? THIS IS THE **TEMPLE** ! YOUR MOTHER AND I HAVE BEEN WORRIED **SICK** ABOUT YOU !

THE CARAVAN LEFT WITHOUT ME. I KNEW I'D BE SAFE HERE, AND THAT YOU'D COME SOONER OR LATER.

AFTER ALL, DIDN'T YOU KNOW I WOULD BE IN MY **FATHER'S** HOUSE ?

ALTHOUGH IT MADE LITTLE SENSE TO ANYONE AT THE TIME, MARY STORED ALL THESE STORIES IN HER HEART.

AND IN THIS WAY, JESUS GREW IN BODY AND SPIRIT, AND WAS LOVED BY GOD AND PEOPLE ALIKE AS THE YEARS WENT BY...

12

'A VOICE IS CALLING IN THE DESERT, PREPARE THE WAY FOR THE LORD... THE WHOLE OF CREATION WILL SEE GOD'S SALVATION.'

IN THE FIFTEENTH YEAR OF THE REIGN OF THE ROMAN EMPEROR TIBERIUS CAESAR – WHEN PONTIUS PILATE WAS GOVERNOR OF JUDEA – THE WORD OF GOD CAME TO JOHN, THE SON OF ELIZABETH AND ZECHARIAH.

THE WHOLE COUNTRY CAME **ALIVE** WITH HIS WORDS, AND PEOPLE CAME FROM FAR AND NEAR JUST TO HEAR HIM SPEAK.

CENTURIES EARLIER, THE PROPHET ISAIAH HAD TOLD OF THE STORY NOW UNFOLDING.

YOU BROOD OF **SNAKES**!

DISASTER IS APPROACHING YOU! IT'S NO USE SAYING 'WE'RE **JEWS**! WE HAVE **ABRAHAM** AS OUR FATHER!' THAT WON'T SAVE YOU! GET DOWN ON YOUR KNEES AND **REPENT**!

IF YOU REPENT YOUR LIVES SHOULD SHOW THE **FRUIT** OF THAT REPENTANCE! LOVE! HONESTY! **KINDNESS**!

BE BAPTIZED IN THE RIVER BY ME, AND CHANGE YOUR LIVES WHILE THERE IS STILL TIME!

BUT I AM A **TAX COLLECTOR**! WE'RE HATED BY JEWS FOR SERVING THE ROMANS, AND BY THE ROMANS FOR BEING TRAITORS TO OUR OWN PEOPLE! HOW CAN **WE** EVER LIVE A GOOD LIFE?

EASILY – JUST DON'T COLLECT MORE THAN YOU HAVE TO. BE HONEST.

YOU SOLDIERS – NO MORE EXTORTION OR BRIBERY. DON'T **LIE** ABOUT PEOPLE!

WE HAVE TO ASK YOU, SIR: ARE YOU THE **MESSIAH**?

ARE YOU THE ONE WE'VE BEEN WAITING FOR?

I ONLY BAPTIZE YOU WITH **WATER**. BUT SOMEONE IS COMING SOON WHO IS FAR MORE POWERFUL THAN I! I AM NOT FIT EVEN TO UNLACE HIS SANDALS!

HE WILL BAPTIZE YOU WITH THE **HOLY SPIRIT**! WITH **FIRE**!

AND SO NEWS OF JOHN SPREAD ACROSS THE LAND, AND MANY CAME TO HIM TO BE BAPTIZED.

JESUS. THE MESSIAH.

ARE YOU STILL HERE? THE OTHERS WENT HOME AGES AGO! MOST PEOPLE LEAVE **EARLY** ON THEIR LAST DAY AT WORK!

I WANTED TO FINISH THE JOISTS BEFORE I LEFT. I CAN'T GO OFF AND LEAVE THE JOB HALF FINISHED.

THERE. THAT SHOULD LAST FOR **CENTURIES.**

WELL, WE'RE CERTAINLY GOING TO MISS YOU. I DON'T KNOW, WORKING AFTER HOURS — YOU'RE AS BAD AS YOUR FATHER!

I'LL TAKE THAT AS A COMPLIMENT — ALTHOUGH BEING BAD ISN'T ONE OF HIS TRAITS!

...SORRY?

A JOKE. DON'T WORRY ABOUT IT.

ARE YOU SURE YOU DON'T WANT TO COME **WITH** ME?

I CAN'T. AND I STILL DON'T UNDERSTAND WHY **YOU** OF ALL PEOPLE WANT TO BE **BAPTIZED**! I MEAN, THE PEOPLE WHO COME TO HIM — MURDERERS, THIEVES, LIARS — I'VE KNOWN YOU YOUR WHOLE LIFE, JESUS, AND YOU'RE... YOU'RE **BETTER** THAN THEM!

I'M GOING TO SEE JOHN, AND I'M **GOING** TO GET BAPTIZED. IN FACT I'M LOOKING FORWARD TO IT! GOODBYE!

THE ACT OF BAPTISM WAS A SYMBOL, AN OUTWARD SIGN OF THE PEOPLE WASHING THEIR GUILT AWAY IN FRONT OF GOD.

JESUS WAS DIFFERENT FROM THE CROWDS WHO FLOCKED TO JOHN TO BE BAPTIZED.

14

JESUS **HAD** NO GUILT. NO SIN. NO SHAME. HE WAS BAPTIZED, NOT TO BE MADE CLEAN BEFORE GOD...

BUT TO BE DOWN IN THE WATER, ALONGSIDE THE BROKEN AND THE SINFUL – **THAT** WAS WHY HE CAME.

IS THAT **JESUS**? WHAT'S **HE** DOING HERE?

MAYBE HE'S COME TO HELP JOHN?

BAPTIZE ME, JOHN.

YOU? WHATEVER **FOR**, JESUS? EVERYONE KNOWS YOU'VE DONE NOTHING WRONG YOUR WHOLE LIFE! THIS IS FOR **SINNERS**! IF ANYTHING **YOU** SHOULD BE BAPTIZING **ME**!

TRUST ME, JOHN. THIS IS THE RIGHT THING TO DO.

BAPTIZE ME.

AND SO JESUS WAS BAPTIZED IN THE RIVER JORDAN.

WHEN ASKED ABOUT IT LATER, JOHN DESCRIBED IT IN THESE WORDS:

'I SAW HEAVEN **OPEN**. A VOICE CRIED OUT – '

THIS IS MY SON, WHOM I LOVE; WITH HIM I AM WELL PLEASED!

'I SAW THE HEAVENS TORN OPEN, AND THE HOLY SPIRIT DESCEND ON JESUS LIKE A DOVE!'

'HE IS THE LAMB OF GOD, COME TO TAKE AWAY THE SINS OF THE WHOLE **WORLD**! I SAY IN TRUTH, THAT THIS MAN IS THE LIVING **SON OF GOD**!'

IMMEDIATELY AFTER HE WAS BAPTIZED, THE SPIRIT TOOK JESUS FAR OUT INTO THE DESERT.

THERE, WITHOUT FOOD, HE STAYED FOR FORTY DAYS AND NIGHTS.

HE BURNED BY DAY...

AND HE FROZE BY NIGHT.

AND THEN, WHEN HE WAS AT HIS WEAKEST AND MOST VULNERABLE, HIS TRIALS BEGAN IN EARNEST.

ALONE, AND FAR FROM FRIENDS, JESUS ENCOUNTERED THE **DEVIL**.

WHO TRIED TO **TEMPT** HIM...

I AM SO HUNGRY. LORD GOD, PLEASE HELP ME WITH THIS HUNGER. THE PAIN IS TOO MUCH...

YOU? **HUNGRY**? WHY, JESUS, IF YOU'RE THE SON OF GOD, WHY DON'T YOU COMMAND THE STONES TO BECOME BREAD?

YOU KNOW THEY WILL. YOU KNOW HOW **GOOD** THEY'LL TASTE.

DO IT. DO IT **NOW**!

IT IS WRITTEN: 'MAN DOESN'T LIVE ON BREAD ALONE, BUT BY THE WORDS THAT COME FROM GOD'S MOUTH.' THEREFORE I WON'T USE GOD'S POWER FOR MY OWN NEEDS.

THEN *LOOK*. I WILL GIVE YOU ALL THE KINGDOMS ON EARTH, IF YOU WILL BOW DOWN AND WORSHIP *ME*!

IT IS WRITTEN: 'WORSHIP ONLY GOD, AND SERVE ONLY *HIM*!'

IF YOU *ARE* THE SON OF GOD, WHY NOT THROW YOURSELF FROM THE HIGHEST ROOF OF THE TEMPLE? SURELY GOD WILL SAVE YOU.

YOU COULD DO ANYTHING YOU *WISHED* AND GOD WOULD SAVE YOU! WHY NOT *DO* IT?

IT IS WRITTEN: 'DO NOT PUT THE LORD YOUR GOD TO THE TEST.'

LEAVE ME, SATAN. I WILL NOT TURN FROM GOD.

AND AS THE DEVIL LEFT, *ANGELS* CAME, AND TENDED TO JESUS IN THE DESERT.

HE HAD NOT GIVEN IN AS *ADAM* HAD. JESUS' WORK ON EARTH COULD BEGIN...

JESUS BEGAN TO SEARCH FOR PEOPLE TO HELP HIM IN HIS WORK.

THE FIRST CHOSEN WERE A GROUP OF FISHERMEN, WORKING THE SHORES OF LAKE GALILEE.

ANDREW! PETER!

FOLLOW ME!

AND AT ONCE THE BROTHERS LEFT THEIR NETS AND FOLLOWED JESUS.

WHERE ARE WE GOING, TEACHER? DO YOU NEED US TO HELP YOU FISH?

IN A MANNER OF SPEAKING.

JAMES AND JOHN! FOLLOW ME, AND I WILL MAKE YOU FISHERS OF **PEOPLE**!

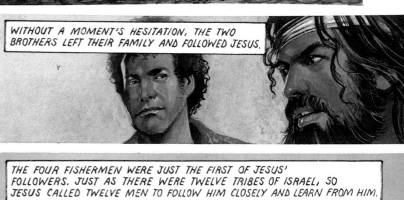

WITHOUT A MOMENT'S HESITATION, THE TWO BROTHERS LEFT THEIR FAMILY AND FOLLOWED JESUS.

THE FOUR FISHERMEN WERE JUST THE FIRST OF JESUS' FOLLOWERS. JUST AS THERE WERE TWELVE TRIBES OF ISRAEL, SO JESUS CALLED TWELVE MEN TO FOLLOW HIM CLOSELY AND LEARN FROM HIM.

THEY WERE CALLED HIS **DISCIPLES**.

MATTHEW, A TAX COLLECTOR.

THOMAS.

JUDAS ISCARIOT.

PHILIP.

SIMON, THE ZEALOT.

JAMES, SON OF ALPHAEUS.

BARTHOLOMEW.

JUDAS, SON OF JAMES.

COMING FROM ALL CLASSES AND WALKS OF LIFE, THEY WOULD STAY WITH JESUS FOR THE REST OF HIS LIFE...

AND SO JESUS BEGAN TO TEACH. AND AS HE SPOKE, PEOPLE FLOCKED TO LISTEN IN THEIR *HUNDREDS*.

HE WAS UNLIKE ANYONE THEY HAD EVER HEARD BEFORE...

BLESSED ARE YOU WHO ARE *POOR*. FOR YOURS IS THE KINGDOM OF GOD. BLESSED ARE YOU WHO ARE *HUNGRY* AND WEEP, FOR YOU WILL BE FED AND SHED TEARS OF JOY!

BLESSED ARE YOU WHO ARE *PEACEMAKERS*, FOR YOU WILL BE GOD'S OWN CHILDREN.

I TELL YOU NOW, *LOVE* YOUR ENEMIES. SHOW KINDNESS TO THOSE WHO HATE YOU. TREAT OTHERS IN THE WAY *YOU* WANT TO BE TREATED.

IF SOMEONE STRIKES YOU ON ONE SIDE OF YOUR FACE, SAY 'HERE, HIT THE OTHER SIDE TOO!'

IF YOU CATCH SOMEONE STEALING YOUR CLOAK, THEN SAY 'HERE, HAVE MY TUNIC AS WELL!'

IF YOU'RE ONLY KIND TO THE PEOPLE WHO ARE KIND TO *YOU*, WHAT'S THE GOOD OF THAT? EVEN MURDERERS TREAT THEIR FRIENDS WELL.

DON'T JUDGE PEOPLE, AND *YOU* WON'T BE JUDGED. *FORGIVE* PEOPLE, AND *YOU* WILL BE FORGIVEN.

IF YOU SHOW KINDNESS TO OTHERS, DO IT *QUIETLY*. DON'T ANNOUNCE YOUR GOOD DEEDS WITH *TRUMPETS* LIKE THE HYPOCRITES.

GOD SEES EVERYTHING.

THERE WERE TWO MAIN RELIGIOUS FACTIONS IN ISRAEL, THE **PHARISEES** AND THE **SADDUCEES**. AND JESUS' WORDS DID NOT GO UNNOTICED BY EITHER...

WHY DO YOU LOOK AT THE BIT OF SAWDUST IN YOUR BROTHER'S EYE, AND FAIL TO SEE YOU HAVE A PLANK OF WOOD IN YOUR OWN? YOU HYPOCRITES! FIRST TAKE THE PLANK OUT OF YOUR **OWN** EYE, AND ONLY **THEN** TELL YOUR BROTHER ABOUT THE SAWDUST IN HIS!

AND **WHEN** YOU PRAY, DON'T BE LIKE THE HYPOCRITES WHO LOVE TO PRAY ON STREET CORNERS, WHERE EVERYONE CAN SEE HOW 'HOLY' THEY ARE.

INSTEAD, GO TO YOUR ROOM, CLOSE THE DOOR, AND PRAY TO GOD LIKE THIS:

PSST!... WHAT DO YOU THINK?

I WONDER BY WHAT **AUTHORITY** HE SAYS THESE THINGS. WHO DOES HE REPRESENT? **US**? THE SADDUCEES? THE **ROMANS** EVEN?

DEAR FATHER, HALLOWED BE YOUR NAME. YOUR KINGDOM COME, YOUR WILL BE DONE ON EARTH AS IT IS IN HEAVEN.

GIVE US TODAY OUR DAILY BREAD, AND FORGIVE US OUR SINS, AS WE FORGIVE THOSE WHO SIN AGAINST US. DO NOT LEAD US INTO TEMPTATION, BUT SAVE US FROM EVIL.

I TELL YOU THE TRUTH: IF ANYONE HEARS MY WORDS AND OBEYS THEM, THEN THEY WILL NEVER KNOW DEATH.

ABRAHAM DIED! **MOSES** DIED, TOO! IS HE SAYING HE IS GREATER THAN ABRAHAM AND MOSES?!

WHO DOES HE THINK HE IS, SPEAKING THIS WAY?!

NO! HE HAS GONE TOO FAR THIS TIME!

NEVER DIE?! OF **COURSE** THEY'LL DIE!

I AM THE LIGHT OF THE WORLD. NO ONE WHO BELIEVES IN ME SHOULD HAVE TO LIVE THEIR LIVES IN DARKNESS.

FROM THIS TIME ON, THE RELIGIOUS LEADERS MADE JESUS THEIR ENEMY, AND BEGAN TO PLOT HIS DESTRUCTION...

JESUS WENT FROM NAZARETH TO THE TOWN OF CAPERNAUM, TO PREACH IN THE SYNAGOGUE.

PEOPLE WERE AMAZED BY THE THINGS HE SAID.

BEWARE OF FALSE TEACHERS. THEY COME TO YOU AS HARMLESS AS SHEEP, BUT INSIDE THEY'RE **WOLVES**, WAITING TO GET OUT!

HA! I KNOW YOU! I SEE YOU I SEE I SEE I SEE **YOU**!

LOOK AT HIM. DON'T YOU KNOW WHO IT IS?! DON'T ANY OF YOU STUPID, WEAK, **FOOLS** KNOW WHAT IT IS YOU HAVE INVITED INTO YOUR HOUSE?!

HAVE YOU COME TO **DESTROY** US, JESUS OF NAZARETH?

OH YES, I KNOW YOUR **NAME**! I KNOW YOUR **TRUE** NAME, I SEE YOUR - YOUR **TRUE** NATURE! OH I DO, INDEED I DO!

YOU ARE GOD'S HOLY ONE!

BE QUIET!

COME OUT, DEMON, AND LEAVE THIS POOR MAN ALONE.

NOOOOO! I WON'T GO, I WON'T -

YAAARGGG!!!

PRAISE GOD. MY MIND - IT'S CLEAR! CLEAR AS FRESH AIR!

HAH! - I CAN'T BELIEVE IT! I'M MYSELF AGAIN! PRAISE GOD!

WHO **IS** HE, THIS JESUS? HE GIVES ORDERS EVEN TO EVIL SPIRITS AND THEY **OBEY** HIM?

AND IN THIS WAY, WORD OF JESUS SPREAD THROUGH THE COUNTRY LIKE WILDFIRE.

HIS REPUTATION AS A HEALER AND TEACHER GREW...

MASTER! THANK YOU FOR COMING! IT'S MY WIFE'S MOTHER. I DON'T KNOW WHAT'S WRONG WITH HER.

IS SHE ILL, PETER?

DYING. SHE'S BURNING WITH FEVER - I DON'T THINK SHE WILL LAST THE NIGHT.

I SEE.

JESUS TOUCHED THE WOMAN'S HAND AND THE FEVER LEFT HER.

THERE. HOW DO YOU FEEL?

OH! I FEEL — I FEEL WONDERFUL!

MY! SO MANY GUESTS IN THE HOUSE!

NOW THEN, WHO'S HUNGRY AND WANTS TO JOIN ME IN SOMETHING TO EAT? I'M STARVING!

JESUS STAYED UP ALL THAT NIGHT, HEALING ANYONE WHO WOULD COME TO HIM.

FROM MILES AROUND, PEOPLE BROUGHT THE SICK AND SUFFERING, AND JESUS HEALED THEM ALL.

YOUR GRANDSON WILL BE FINE NOW, BUT YOU MUST TELL NO ONE WHAT HAPPENED HERE TONIGHT.

THEN WHAT THE PEOPLE SAY MUST BE TRUE - YOU ARE THE SON OF GOD!

AGAIN, I TELL YOU, TELL NO ONE ABOUT THIS!

THE JEWS WERE WAITING FOR THE MESSIAH TO OVERTHROW THE ROMANS. JESUS KNEW GOD HAD OTHER PLANS...

NEAR THE SHORES OF THE LAKE THEY WERE MET BY A ROMAN OFFICIAL, SENT BY THE CENTURION OF THE NEARBY GARRISON.

THE CENTURION HAD A SERVANT WHO WAS SICK, AND JESUS HAD BEEN ASKED TO HEAL HIM.

MY MASTER SAYS NOT TO CONCERN YOURSELF WITH MAKING THE JOURNEY TO VISIT US.

WHY NOT? IS THE SICK MAN **WELL** AGAIN?

NO SIR, HE IS **DYING**. BUT MY MASTER GIVES THIS MESSAGE:

'IF YOU SIMPLY SAY THE WORD, MY SERVANT WILL BE HEALED. I TOO AM A MAN UNDER AUTHORITY. IF I TELL A SOLDIER "DO THIS", I KNOW IT WILL BE DONE. I SEE THAT SAME AUTHORITY IN YOU.'

SUCH **FAITH**...

I HAVE NEVER SEEN SUCH FAITH IN ALL OF **ISRAEL**; AND YET HERE IT IS COMING FROM A **ROMAN**...

GO HOME. THE MAN **WILL** BE HEALED JUST AS YOU SAID.

MASTER, I'VE DECIDED TO **FOLLOW** YOU, BUT FIRST LET ME SAY GOODBYE TO MY FAMILY.

NO ONE WHO PUTS A HAND TO THE PLOUGH AND LOOKS BACK IS FIT FOR THE KINGDOM OF GOD.

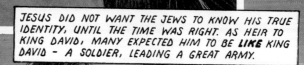

JESUS DID NOT WANT THE JEWS TO KNOW HIS TRUE IDENTITY, UNTIL THE TIME WAS RIGHT. AS HEIR TO KING DAVID, MANY EXPECTED HIM TO BE **LIKE** KING DAVID – A SOLDIER, LEADING A GREAT ARMY.

THE **ZEALOTS**, A GROUP OF FREEDOM FIGHTERS, WERE PLANNING TO OVERTHROW THE ROMANS AT ANY MOMENT, AND NEWS OF THE MESSIAH WOULD BE THE SPARK THEY NEEDED TO IGNITE THE REBELLION.

AS THEY LEFT CAPERNAUM, JESUS, WORN OUT FROM THE JOURNEY, FELL INTO A DEEP SLEEP...

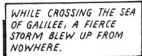

WHILE CROSSING THE SEA OF GALILEE, A FIERCE STORM BLEW UP FROM NOWHERE.

SOON EVEN THE HARDENED FISHERMEN AMONG THE DISCIPLES WERE FEARFUL FOR THEIR LIVES!

ANDREW, WE'RE TAKING IN WATER! THE MAST WILL BREAK! WAKE HIM!

YOU WAKE HIM!

UNLESS WE DO SOMETHING WE'LL ALL DROWN! *SOMEONE* HAS TO WAKE THE MASTER!!

HOW CAN HE SLEEP THROUGH THIS?!

JESUS! *SAVE* US! THE BOAT IS GOING DOWN!!

MMPH? WHAT BOAT?

YOU OF LITTLE FAITH, WHY ARE YOU SO AFRAID?

STORM! BE *QUIET*!

HMPH. THAT'S BETTER.

WHAT KIND OF MAN IS THIS?

EVEN THE WIND AND WAVES OBEYED JESUS.

LANDING ON THE FAR SIDE OF THE SEA, JESUS HAD NO SOONER STEPPED FROM THE BOAT, WHEN HE HEARD THE STRANGEST NOISE...

NOISE, WE HEAR.

SHUT UP!

My friends, we have guests!

WORM. YOU WORM.

PEOPLE ON THE BEACH.

I KNOW. I KNOW THERE ARE.

SMASH THEIR BOAT UP!

JESUS! SON OF THE MOST HIGH GOD! What DO You WANT WITH US?!!

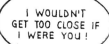

MY PIGS!
MY PIGS!

IT WAS THAT MAN FROM **NAZARETH** THEY'RE TALKING ABOUT – THAT **JESUS**! HE WAS TALKING TO OLD LEGION, AND HE DID SOMETHING TO MY PIGS AND NOW THEY'RE DROWNED!!

I WAS WARNED ABOUT HIM. HE'S CAUSED TROUBLE ALL AROUND GALILEE. WE DON'T WANT HIS SORT **HERE**.

SEE TO IT HE DOESN'T **STAY**, HMM?

RETURNING TO NAZARETH, JESUS WENT TO THE SYNAGOGUE ON THE SABBATH, AS WAS HIS CUSTOM, TO READ ALOUD AND TEACH.

HE CHOSE THE SCROLLS CONTAINING THE WORDS OF THE PROPHET ISAIAH, WHICH SPOKE OF GOD'S SERVANT, THE MESSIAH, AND BEGAN TO READ –

'THE SPIRIT OF THE LORD IS UPON ME, BECAUSE HE HAS CHOSEN ME TO PREACH GOOD NEWS TO THE POOR.'

'HE HAS SENT ME TO ANNOUNCE FREEDOM FOR PRISONERS, AND RECOVERY OF SIGHT TO THE BLIND.'

'TO RELEASE THE OPPRESSED, TO ANNOUNCE THE YEAR OF THE LORD'S FAVOUR.'

THAT'S IT? JUST THAT SHORT SEGMENT?

IT'LL BE INTERESTING TO HEAR WHAT HE HAS TO **SAY** ABOUT IT.

JESUS ROLLED UP THE SCROLL AND BEGAN TO ADDRESS THE PEOPLE.

TODAY THIS PROPHECY HAS COME *TRUE*, AS YOU HEARD IT BEING READ.

WHAT?

TRUE?

HAS HE LOST HIS MIND?!

WAIT A MINUTE, JESUS. ARE YOU SAYING THAT *YOU* ARE THE CHOSEN SERVANT OF GOD?

JESUS, WE'VE KNOWN YOU SINCE YOU WERE A CHILD — YOU BUILT MY HOUSE FOR ME — HOW CAN *YOU* BE GOD'S CHOSEN ONE?

NO PROPHET IS EVER RESPECTED IN HIS HOME TOWN.

WHEN *ELIJAH* PREACHED, THERE WERE *MANY* WIDOWS IN ISRAEL, YET HE HELPED ONE FROM *SIDON*.

WHEN *ELISHA* PREACHED THERE WERE *MANY* LEPERS IN ISRAEL, YET ONLY A *SYRIAN* WAS HEALED.

HE'S SAYING THAT GOD WILL SEND THE MESSIAH TO *FOREIGNERS* INSTEAD OF JEWS!

BLASPHEMY!

KILL HIM!

DON'T LET HIM GET AWAY!

DON'T CARE *WHOSE* SON HE IS!

IT'S *DISGUSTING*! IT'S *OBSCENE*!

STONE HIM!

BUT AS THE CROWD GRABBED AT JESUS, MEANING TO *KILL* HIM, HE WALKED THROUGH THEM COMPLETELY UNHARMED, AND WENT ON HIS WAY.

27

PHARISEES, TEACHERS OF THE LAW AND ORDINARY PEOPLE CAME FROM ALL OVER JUDEA, EVEN FROM JERUSALEM, TO HEAR JESUS TALK.

AND AS HE TAUGHT, HE HEALED PEOPLE FROM EVERY SICKNESS.

HE'D BETTER *BE* HERE THIS TIME!

IT'S NOT *MY* FAULT WE KEEP MISSING HIM. *YOU* WERE THE ONE WHO SAID WE SHOULD GO TO THE ROMAN GARRISON!

OH NO! THESE PEOPLE HAVE BEEN WAITING FOR *HOURS*. THERE'S NO *WAY* WE'RE GOING TO GET TO SEE HIM!

WELL, THAT'S IT THEN. WE'VE DONE ALL WE CAN.

NO! WE'VE BROUGHT HIM THIS FAR. WE CAN'T JUST GIVE UP NOW. WE'RE SO *CLOSE*!

WAIT! I'VE HAD AN IDEA.

OH PLEASE, NOT ANOTHER ONE.

ALL RIGHT THEN, WE'RE ON THE ROOF. *NOW* WHAT?

YOU'LL *LIKE* THIS PART.

IF WE CAN'T GET HIM IN THROUGH THE *DOOR* THEN WE'LL HAVE TO *MAKE* AN ENTRANCE OF OUR OWN!

BUT JESUS, JOHN'S DISCIPLES FASTED, AND SO DO THE PHARISEES — *YOURS* NEVER STOP EATING AND DRINKING!

DO YOU MAKE WEDDING GUESTS FAST AT A WEDDING RECEPTION? NO, OF COURSE NOT.

BUT BEFORE LONG, THE BRIDEGROOM WILL BE TAKEN AWAY, AND *THEN* THEY WILL FAST!

MORE AND MORE PEOPLE CAME TO SEE JESUS, ASKING HIM TO HEAL THEIR SICK.

MASTER, A MAN CALLED JAIRUS, THE LEADER OF THE LOCAL SYNAGOGUE, ASKS FOR YOU.

MY LITTLE DAUGHTER IS DYING! PLEASE, SHE IS ALL WE HAVE IN THE WORLD. IF YOU PUT YOUR HANDS ON HER I KNOW SHE WILL *LIVE*!

THE DISCIPLES SOON HAD THEIR HANDS FULL CONTROLLING THE CROWDS.

AMONG THE CROWD WAS A WOMAN, WHO HAD SUFFERED FROM CONSTANT BLEEDING FOR YEARS. NO DOCTOR COULD HELP HER. BUT SHE THOUGHT – 'IF ONLY I COULD TOUCH JESUS' CLOAK I WOULD BE WELL AGAIN.'

EVENTUALLY SHE REACHED JESUS...

AND AS SHE BRUSHED HIS CLOAK WITH HER FINGERTIPS –

– SHE WAS *HEALED*.

WHO *TOUCHED* ME?

SOMEONE TOUCHED MY CLOAK. I FELT POWER GO OUT FROM ME.

THE WOMAN, WHO WAS FULL OF FEAR, TOLD JESUS EVERYTHING.

DAUGHTER, YOUR FAITH HAS HEALED YOU.

GO IN PEACE, AND KNOW THAT YOU ARE FREE FROM YOUR SUFFERING.

SEEING THIS ONLY GIVES ME MORE HOPE, JESUS. BUT WE MUST HURRY; PLEASE, COME WITH ME.

JAIRUS! I'M SO SORRY, MY FRIEND, YOUR DAUGHTER HAS DIED. HE CAN'T HELP YOU NOW.

JAIRUS, *LISTEN* TO ME! DON'T BE AFRAID. JUST *BELIEVE* !

JESUS DID NOT LET ANYONE FOLLOW HIM, EXCEPT PETER, JAMES AND JOHN. BUT AT THE HOUSE A CROWD OF MOURNERS HAD GATHERED.

WHAT'S ALL THE COMMOTION ABOUT? GET OUT! THE CHILD IS NOT DEAD, BUT SLEEPING.

JESUS, LISTEN, PEOPLE ARE *LAUGHING* AT YOU.

MY CHILD, GET UP.

HMM?

IS IT THAT TIME ALREADY?

HOW CAN I EVER THANK YOU, JESUS?

GIVE HER SOMETHING TO *EAT* — SHE MUST BE *STARVING*. AND DON'T TELL ANYONE WHAT HAS HAPPENED.

A CONSTANT STREAM OF PEOPLE CAME TO JESUS TO SEEK HEALING AND COMFORT. AMONG THE CROWD ONE DAY WERE TWO OF JOHN THE BAPTIST'S FOLLOWERS.

TEACHER, TWO OF JOHN'S DISCIPLES ARE HERE TO SEE YOU.

WE HAVE A MESSAGE FROM JOHN IN PRISON: 'ARE YOU THE ONE GOD PROMISED TO US OR SHOULD WE EXPECT SOMEONE ELSE?'

TELL JOHN WHAT YOU'VE SEEN: 'THE BLIND CAN SEE, THE LAME WALK, THE LEPERS ARE CURED, THE DEAF HEAR, THE DEAD ARE RAISED UP AND GOOD NEWS IS PREACHED TO THE POOR.' HE WILL UNDERSTAND WHAT THIS MEANS.

AND SEND JOHN MY GREETINGS...

AS JOHN'S DISCIPLES WERE LEAVING, JESUS BEGAN TO SPEAK TO THE CROWD ABOUT JOHN.

WHEN YOU WENT OUT INTO THE DESERT TO LISTEN TO JOHN, WHAT DID YOU *EXPECT* TO FIND?

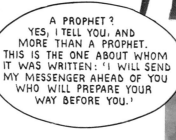

A PROPHET? YES, I TELL YOU, AND MORE THAN A PROPHET. THIS IS THE ONE ABOUT WHOM IT WAS WRITTEN: 'I WILL SEND MY MESSENGER AHEAD OF YOU WHO WILL PREPARE YOUR WAY BEFORE YOU.'

I TELL YOU THE TRUTH. JOHN IS THE GREATEST OF ALL THE PROPHETS. AND YET THE VERY *LEAST* PERSON WHO BELIEVES MY WORDS WILL BE GREATER THAN HIM!

JOHN THE BAPTIST HAD SPOKEN OUT AGAINST KING HEROD ANTIPAS, SON OF THE KING WHO HAD ORDERED THE SLAUGHTER OF INNOCENT CHILDREN SOON AFTER JESUS WAS BORN.

JOHN HAD PUBLICLY DENOUNCED THE KING FOR MARRYING HIS BROTHER'S WIFE, HERODIAS, AS THIS WAS AGAINST THE LAW OF MOSES. JOHN WAS DRAGGED OFF TO PRISON THE SAME DAY.

WHILE THE KING DECIDED WHAT TO DO WITH JOHN, HE THREW A PARTY TO CELEBRATE HIS **BIRTHDAY.**

THE MAIN ATTRACTION AT THE PARTY WAS HERODIAS'S DAUGHTER, SALOME, WHO DANCED FOR HEROD AND HIS GUESTS.

HEROD WAS SO PLEASED WITH SALOME THAT HE MADE A RASH PROMISE TO HER, IN FRONT OF HIS ENTIRE COURT...

ASK ANYTHING OF ME, AND IT SHALL BE YOURS!

ANYTHING?

NAME IT!

VERY WELL.

GIVE ME THE HEAD OF JOHN THE BAPTIST, HACKED OFF AND ON A SILVER PLATE.

THERE WAS NO WAY HEROD COULD BACK DOWN IN FRONT OF SO MANY IMPORTANT PEOPLE.

AND BESIDES, HIS WIFE HAD PUT THE GIRL UP TO IT, HE WAS SURE. HERODIAS **HATED** JOHN.

DO AS SHE SAYS.

HAVE JOHN BEHEADED AND HIS HEAD SERVED ON A SILVER PLATE. HIS DISCIPLES MAY HAVE THE REST OF THE BODY TO BURY AS THEY SEE FIT.

ONE DAY, AS JESUS WALKED ALONG THE SHORES OF LAKE GALILEE, THE CROWDS BECAME SO LARGE HE HAD TO STAND IN A FISHERMAN'S BOAT TO MAKE HIMSELF HEARD.

THE KINGDOM OF GOD IS LIKE THIS:

THERE WAS ONCE A FARMER WHO WENT TO SOW SEED. AS HE SCATTERED THE SEED, SOME FELL ON THE PATH AND BIRDS CAME AND ATE IT UP STRAIGHT AWAY.

'OTHER SEED FELL AMONG THORNS, WHICH CHOKED THE PLANTS BEFORE THEY HAD A CHANCE TO GROW PROPERLY.

'THE SEED IS GOD'S MESSAGE. SOME PEOPLE IGNORE IT; SOME TAKE TO IT AT ONCE, BUT IT NEVER TAKES ROOT. OTHERS BELIEVE FOR A WHILE, BUT LIFE'S WORRIES CROWD IN AND THEY FALL AWAY, BUT OTHERS ALLOW IT TO GROW IN THEIR LIVES AND FLOURISH.'

'SOME SEED FELL ON ROCKY GROUND AND SPRANG UP IN THE THIN SOIL. WHEN THE SUN CAME UP THE PLANTS WITHERED AWAY.

'BUT OTHER SEED FELL ON THE **GOOD** SOIL, WHERE IT PRODUCED A FINE CROP, MANY TIMES OVER.

THE KINGDOM OF HEAVEN IS LIKE THIS: ONCE UPON A TIME A MAN WAS DIGGING IN A FIELD WHEN HE STRUCK A HARD OBJECT...

'THE FIELD WOULD COST ALL HE HAD, SO HE SOLD EVERYTHING TO RAISE ENOUGH MONEY. THE MAN WAS FULL OF JOY FOR THE TREASURE WOULD BE HIS.'

'HE DUG UP A GOLD JAR FULL OF TREASURE — RINGS AND GOLD COINS. IF HE COULD BUY THE FIELDS HE WOULD RIGHTLY OWN THE TREASURE.

LATER, JESUS WAS DINING AT THE HOUSE OF A PHARISEE AND TOLD ANOTHER STORY ABOUT THE KINGDOM OF HEAVEN.

A MAN ONCE THREW A FABULOUS FEAST, A WONDERFUL BANQUET FOR ALL HIS FRIENDS.

'BUT THEY WERE SO SPOILT AND UNGRATEFUL THAT ON THE DAY OF THE FEAST THEY ALL MADE EXCUSES AND DIDN'T COME.

'SO THE MAN SENT HIS SERVANT OUT ONTO THE STREETS TO CALL THE HOMELESS, THE BEGGARS, LEPERS AND CRIPPLES, AND INVITED **THEM** TO HIS HOME FOR THE FEAST.

'THE MAN SAID: "NOT ONE OF THE GUESTS I FIRST INVITED WILL GET EVEN A **TASTE** OF MY BANQUET."'

34

AS JESUS' NOTORIETY INCREASED HE WAS INVITED TO THE HOMES OF RELIGIOUS LEADERS WHO WANTED TO HEAR FOR THEMSELVES WHAT HE HAD TO SAY.

ONE EVENING A WOMAN HEARD HE WOULD BE DINING NEARBY AND MADE HER WAY TO THE HOUSE.

SHE WAITED IN THE DOORWAY FOR THE RIGHT MOMENT TO APPROACH JESUS. SHE WAS WELL KNOWN AS A PROSTITUTE AND, AWARE OF HER SHAME, DARED NOT LOOK JESUS IN THE FACE.

INSTEAD, SHE BENT DOWN AND, CRYING BITTERLY, WASHED HIS FEET.

WITHOUT A WORD SHE POURED EXPENSIVE PERFUME ONTO HIS FEET AND DRIED THEM WITH HER HAIR.

DOESN'T HE KNOW WHAT SHE IS, AND HOW SHE GOT THE MONEY FOR THAT PERFUME?

IF HE **WERE** A PROPHET HE WOULD KNOW WHAT KIND OF WOMAN SHE IS — A SINNER.

IF TWO MEN OWED MONEY — ONE MAN A HUGE SUM, THE OTHER MUCH LESS — AND THE DEBTS WERE CANCELLED, WHO WOULD BE THE MOST GRATEFUL?

THIS WOMAN HAS SHOWN **REAL** LOVE. YOU DID NOT EVEN DO ME THE COURTESY OF GIVING ME WATER TO WASH MY FEET, BUT SHE WET MY FEET WITH HER TEARS AND DRIED THEM WITH HER HAIR.

HER MANY SINS HAVE BEEN FORGIVEN — FOR SHE LOVED MUCH. BUT HE WHO HAS BEEN FORGIVEN LITTLE, LOVES LITTLE.

YOUR SINS ARE FORGIVEN. YOUR FAITH HAS SAVED YOU. GO IN PEACE.

CAN YOU BELIEVE HE SAID THAT TO **HER**?! WHO IS THIS THAT EVEN FORGIVES SINS?

THE WOMAN LEFT KNOWING HER LIFE HAD BEEN CHANGED FOR EVER.

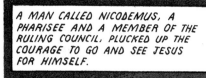

A MAN CALLED NICODEMUS, A PHARISEE AND A MEMBER OF THE RULING COUNCIL, PLUCKED UP THE COURAGE TO GO AND SEE JESUS FOR HIMSELF.

HE WENT IN THE MIDDLE OF THE NIGHT...

WHEN EVERYONE ELSE WAS FAST ASLEEP, AND NO ONE WOULD KNOW WHERE HE'D BEEN.

> YAWN <
A BIT LATE, ISN'T IT?

I HAVE TO *SPEAK* TO YOU. I *KNOW* YOU'VE COME FROM GOD ~ HOW *ELSE* COULD YOU DO THE MIRACULOUS THINGS YOU'VE DONE?

I TELL YOU THE TRUTH ~ *NO ONE* CAN SEE THE KINGDOM OF GOD, UNLESS THEY ARE BORN AGAIN.

'BORN' AGAIN? HOW CAN I BE BORN AGAIN AT *MY* AGE? I CAN'T GO BACK TO MY MOTHER'S WOMB.

UNLESS YOU ARE BORN OF WATER AND THE SPIRIT YOU CANNOT ENTER THE KINGDOM OF GOD. FLESH GIVES BIRTH TO FLESH, BUT THE SPIRIT GIVES BIRTH TO SPIRIT.

THE SON OF MAN MUST BE LIFTED UP, SO THAT EVERYONE WHO BELIEVES IN HIM MAY HAVE ETERNAL LIFE.

GOD LOVES THE WORLD SO MUCH, THAT HE SENT HIS ONLY *SON* SO THAT WHOEVER BELIEVES IN HIM WILL NOT DIE, BUT LIVE FOR EVER.

A GREAT LIGHT HAS COME INTO THE WORLD, BUT EVIL PEOPLE LOVE THE DARKNESS, BECAUSE IT HIDES THEIR DEEDS.

BUT IF YOU LIVE BY THE *TRUTH*, YOU WILL COME INTO THE LIGHT, SO THAT ALL CAN SEE WHAT HAS BEEN DONE THROUGH GOD.

JESUS WENT UP TO JERUSALEM, AND WHILE ON HIS WAY TO A PASSOVER FEAST PASSED THE POOL AT BETHESDA. ALL MANNER OF SICK AND DISABLED PEOPLE WERE THERE TO WASH IN THE POOL, BELIEVING THE WATER TO HAVE HEALING POWERS.

IT WAS THE SABBATH, THE DAY OF REST. ONE MAN CAUGHT JESUS' EYE.

YOU HAVE BEEN ILL A LONG TIME. DO YOU WANT TO GET WELL?

OF COURSE I DO! BUT I HAVE NO ONE TO HELP ME INTO THE POOL.

EVERY TIME THE WATERS STIR I TRY TO GET IN, BUT OTHERS GET THERE FIRST.

- PICK UP YOUR MAT -

AND WALK.

IN THAT CASE, GET UP!

THIS IS INCREDIBLE! I THOUGHT I'D NEVER WALK AGAIN EVER! NOT EVER!

YOU THERE! JUST WHAT DO YOU THINK YOU'RE DOING?

IT'S THE SABBATH! YOU'RE FORBIDDEN TO DO ANY WORK, AND THAT INCLUDES CARRYING MATS!

BUT THE MAN WHO JUST HEALED ME TOLD ME TO PICK UP MY MAT, AND WALK...

SO I DID - FOR THE FIRST TIME IN 38 YEARS!

THIS BLASPHEMY GOES TOO FAR! YOU'RE FORBIDDEN TO WORK ON THE SABBATH, AND THAT INCLUDES HEALING PEOPLE! ARE YOU MOCKING US ON PURPOSE?!

MY FATHER IS ALWAYS AT HIS WORK, EVEN ON THE SABBATH, AND IN THE SAME WAY I'M AT WORK TOO.

JESUS WENT TO SYCHAR, A TOWN IN SAMARIA NEAR THE LAND WHERE JOSEPH HAD LIVED CENTURIES BEFORE. TIRED FROM HIS TRAVELS, JESUS SAT DOWN BY THE WELL TO REST.

A SAMARITAN WOMAN APPROACHED TO DRAW WATER.

I AM THIRSTY. WOULD YOU BE KIND ENOUGH TO GIVE ME A DRINK?

YOU'RE SPEAKING TO *ME*? THERE'S A FIRST! A JEW TALKING TO A *SAMARITAN*. I THOUGHT IT WAS AGAINST YOUR RELIGION.

IF YOU KNEW WHAT GOD COULD GIVE YOU, YOU WOULD ASK FOR *LIVING* WATER.

ANYONE WHO DRINKS THIS WATER HERE WILL BE THIRSTY AGAIN, BUT WHOEVER DRINKS THE WATER *I* GIVE WILL NEVER BE THIRSTY AGAIN.

PLEASE, *GIVE* ME THIS WATER, SO I WON'T HAVE TO KEEP COMING BACK HERE!

GO, GET YOUR HUSBAND, AND BRING HIM HERE.

I HAVE NO HUSBAND.

YOU'VE HAD FIVE HUSBANDS, AND THE MAN YOU'RE LIVING WITH NOW ISN'T YOUR HUSBAND.

HOW DID YOU *KNOW* THAT? ARE YOU A PROPHET? I KNOW THE *MESSIAH* IS COMING. WHEN HE ARRIVES, HE WILL EXPLAIN EVERYTHING TO US.

I, WHO SPEAK TO YOU NOW, AM HE.

THE WOMAN RAN BACK TO THE TOWN TO TELL THE PEOPLE THERE OF THE MAN SHE HAD JUST MET – A MAN WHO KNEW EVERYTHING ABOUT HER.

MANY OF THE SAMARITANS CAME TO BELIEVE IN JESUS AND ACKNOWLEDGED THAT HE WAS INDEED THE MESSIAH SENT BY GOD.

AT THIS TIME, JESUS APPOINTED ANOTHER SEVENTY-TWO FOLLOWERS AND SENT THEM OUT TWO BY TWO TO EVERY TOWN AND VILLAGE HE WAS ABOUT TO VISIT.

WHEN YOU ENTER A TOWN AND ARE **WELCOMED**, STAY THERE. HEAL THE SICK AND TELL THEM THE KINGDOM OF GOD IS NEAR.

THE HARVEST IS PLENTIFUL, BUT THE WORKERS ARE FEW. GO! I'M SENDING YOU OUT LIKE NEWBORN LAMBS INTO A WORLD FULL OF WOLVES.

WHOEVER LISTENS TO YOU, LISTENS TO ME. WHOEVER REJECTS YOU, REJECTS THE ONE WHO SENT ME!

'IF YOU NEED HELP — ASK!'

'IMAGINE YOU HAVE A FRIEND, AND YOU WAKE THEM UP IN THE MIDDLE OF THE NIGHT AND SAY; "WE'VE HAD UNEXPECTED GUESTS AND HAVE RUN OUT OF FOOD — CAN I BORROW THREE LOAVES OF BREAD?"'

YOUR FRIEND SAYS: 'GO AWAY! WE'RE ALL IN BED AND YOU'LL WAKE THE CHILDREN!' AND YET, IF YOU KEEP ASKING, HE STILL **MAY** GET UP AND GIVE YOU WHAT YOU WANT —

NOT **BECAUSE** HE'S YOUR FRIEND, BUT BECAUSE OF YOUR SHEER **AUDACITY.** BECAUSE YOU KEEP ON ASKING AND WON'T KEEP QUIET!

SO I SAY, **ASK**, AND IT WILL BE GIVEN TO YOU. **LOOK**, AND YOU'LL FIND. **KNOCK**, AND THE DOOR WILL BE OPENED TO YOU.

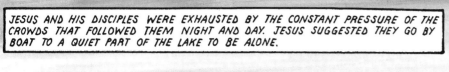

JESUS AND HIS DISCIPLES WERE EXHAUSTED BY THE CONSTANT PRESSURE OF THE CROWDS THAT FOLLOWED THEM NIGHT AND DAY. JESUS SUGGESTED THEY GO BY BOAT TO A QUIET PART OF THE LAKE TO BE ALONE.

BUT SEEING THEM PASS BY, HUGE CROWDS OF PEOPLE BEGAN TO FOLLOW THE BOAT WHEREVER IT WENT.

DESPITE HIS NEED TO REST, JESUS' HEART WAS FILLED WITH COMPASSION, AND HE ASKED FOR THE BOAT TO BE PUT ASHORE SO THAT HE MIGHT HEAL THEIR SICK.

JESUS!

MY BABY! PLEASE HELP ME!

PLEASE, LORD! HELP US!

JESUS, MY FATHER IS DYING!

MY WIFE!

I KNEW YOU WOULDN'T DESERT US!

AFTER HE HAD FINISHED HEALING THEIR SICK, HE TAUGHT THEM ABOUT THE KINGDOM OF GOD, WELL INTO THE EARLY EVENING.

THE CROWD NUMBERED AT LEAST 5,000 PEOPLE.

MASTER, IT'S GETTING LATE. WE'RE IN THE MIDDLE OF NOWHERE AND THESE PEOPLE NEED TO EAT SOON. WHY NOT TELL THEM TO GO AND FIND SOME FOOD?

I HAVE A BETTER IDEA. WHY DON'T YOU FEED THEM?

HOW MUCH FOOD HAVE WE GOT?

FIVE LOAVES OF BREAD, AND TWO FISH.

THEN THAT WILL HAVE TO BE ENOUGH.

JESUS PRAYED A PRAYER OF THANKS FOR THE FOOD, AND THEN HAD THE DISCIPLES PASS IT OUT TO THE CROWD.

I'M TELLING YOU, THIS IS HIM! THE MESSIAH! WHO ELSE COULD DO THIS?

WE SHOULD MAKE HIM OUR KING. WITH HIS POWER WE COULD KICK OUT THE ROMANS!

INCREDIBLY, THERE WAS ENOUGH FOOD FOR EVERYONE. THERE WAS SO MUCH FOOD, THAT AFTER EVERYONE HAD EATEN UNTIL THEY WERE FULL, THE DISCIPLES WERE ABLE TO FILL A BASKET EACH WITH FOOD THAT WENT UNEATEN.

42

LEAVING THE CROWDS BEHIND, JESUS FINALLY FOUND THE TIME TO BE BY HIMSELF.

SENDING HIS DISCIPLES ON TO THE TOWN OF BETHSAIDA, HE WENT UP INTO THE MOUNTAINS TO PRAY.

IT WAS EARLY EVENING WHEN HE CAME DOWN TO THE LAKE AGAIN, AND SAW THE DISCIPLES SLOWLY MAKING THEIR WAY BY BOAT TOWARDS HIM.

THEY SEEMED TO BE HAVING SOME *DIFFICULTY.*

THE WIND IS *AGAINST* US! I DOUBT WE'LL MAKE IT!

STOP MOANING THOMAS, AND *ROW* HARDER!

STOP FIGHTING, THE *LOT* OF YOU, AND PUT SOME EFFORT INTO IT!

LOOK! IT'S THE MASTER! HE'S —

HE'S *WALKING ON THE LAKE!*

THAT'S NOT JESUS, IT'S A *GHOST!*

GOD, HELP US! WE'RE DOOMED! HE'LL *DROWN* US ALL!

DON'T BE FRIGHTENED, PETER. IT'S ME, *JESUS.*

IN THAT CASE, I'M GOING TO MEET HIM! HOLD MY CLOAK, JUDAS!

OF COURSE I'M NOT SURE, WHY SHOULD I —

ARE YOU *SURE* ABOUT THIS?

HELP ME! I CAN'T SWIM!

YOU'RE SAFE, PETER.

THE WINDS DROPPED. CALM RETURNED. AND AS THE BOAT SLIPPED THROUGH THE WATER THE DISCIPLES WORSHIPPED THEIR LORD, NOW KNOWING FOR SURE THAT HE WAS THE SON OF GOD.

ON REACHING SHORE THEY WERE GREETED BY A CROWD OF PEOPLE, EAGER FOR MORE MIRACLES.

ARE THEY *STILL* HERE?

TEACHER, WHAT DO WE HAVE TO DO IN ORDER TO DO GOD'S WILL?

ALL GOD WANTS IS FOR YOU TO BELIEVE IN THE MAN HE *SENT* TO YOU.

YOU'VE COME BACK TODAY LOOKING FOR MORE BREAD. YOU ATE THE BREAD AND FISH YESTERDAY, AND NOW WANT TO SEE ANOTHER *MIRACLE.*

I AM THE BREAD OF LIFE. WHOEVER COMES TO ME WILL NEVER GO HUNGRY. IF ANYONE EATS THE BREAD I GIVE, HE WILL NEVER DIE — BUT I WILL RAISE HIM BACK TO LIFE ON THE LAST DAY.

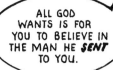

COME ON, DO ANOTHER MIRACLE! DO THAT TRICK WITH THE BREAD AGAIN!

YOUR ANCESTORS ATE *MANNA*, WHEN THEY ESCAPED FROM EGYPT — BUT IN THE END DIED, AS ALL PEOPLE DO.

I AM THE *LIVING* BREAD. THE BREAD I WILL GIVE YOU IS MY *FLESH.* WHOEVER EATS MY FLESH AND DRINKS MY BLOOD WILL NOT DIE, BUT LIVE FOR EVER.

THIS IS TOO DEMANDING, TOO DIFFICULT!

MIRACLES OR NO MIRACLES, YOU WON'T CATCH *ME* DOING A THING LIKE THAT!

I CAN'T FOLLOW HIM ANY LONGER — EVEN IF HE CAN PERFORM MIRACLES.

AND WHAT OF YOU *TWELVE*? WILL YOU REJECT ME TOO?

LORD, WHO *ELSE* WOULD WE FOLLOW? WE BELIEVE AND KNOW THAT YOU ARE THE HOLY ONE OF GOD.

AND YET, ONE OF YOU IS A *DEVIL* — ONE OF YOU TWELVE WILL SOON BETRAY ME.

There was once a man who had two sons. The younger said, 'Father, I can't wait until you're dead. Give me my share of your property **NOW!**'

'And so, while the elder son worked hard for his father every day as he'd always done, the younger son sold the land he had inherited.

'All he wanted was the money, and as soon as he got his hands on it, he set off for the big city, without a second thought for the life he'd left behind...

'And there he spent the **LOT** on drink, parties, prostitutes and gambling. He lived for the moment and made many new friends.

'But it didn't last. The money ran out, and his new "friends" dropped him as quickly as they had taken him up.

'He was left with nothing.

'In desperation he took a job looking after pigs, and was forced to eat their food just to survive.

What are you looking at?

'Eventually he came to his senses and realized he had to return home.

'His father saw him in the distance and, full of compassion, ran to meet him.

Father, forgive me. I am no longer worthy to be called your son. Please take me back - let me work as one of your servants.

Nonsense! This is a time for celebration - let's feast! I want everyone to know the good news.

How can you **DO** this? He's treated you like a **FOOL!** Not **ONCE** have you had a party for **ME**, and I've served you **FAITHFULLY!**

But the father said, 'My son, you are **ALWAYS** with me, and everything I have is **YOURS.** But we must be glad; your brother was dead, but is alive again. He was lost, but now is found.'

YOU SEEM VERY **CONFIDENT**, JESUS. SO **TELL** ME, WHAT MUST **I** DO TO INHERIT ETERNAL LIFE?

YOU HAVE READ THE SCRIPTURES. WHAT DO **YOU** THINK THEY SAY?

'LOVE THE LORD YOUR GOD WITH ALL YOUR HEART, SOUL AND MIND, AND LOVE YOUR NEIGHBOUR AS YOURSELF.'

DO THIS AND YOU WILL LIVE.

BUT WHO **IS** MY NEIGHBOUR?

LISTEN. I'LL TELL YOU.

THERE WAS A MAN, A JEW, TRAVELLING ALONE ON THE STEEP AND DANGEROUS ROAD FROM JERUSALEM TO JERICHO.

'SUDDENLY HE WAS SET UPON BY ROBBERS.

'THEY STOLE ALL HE HAD, BEAT HIM VICIOUSLY AND LEFT HIM FOR DEAD.'

'A **PRIEST** HAPPENED TO PASS BY LATER THAT DAY, BUT DID NOTHING TO HELP THE MAN, NOT WANTING TO GET INVOLVED...

'LIKEWISE, A **LEVITE** CAME BY, BUT CROSSED OVER TO THE OTHER SIDE OF THE ROAD, WANTING NOTHING TO DO WITH THE DYING MAN.

'FINALLY, A **SAMARITAN** PASSED. BREAKING ALL TABOOS HE STOPPED TO HELP...

'AND SAVED THE MAN'S LIFE.

'SEEING HOW BADLY THE MAN WAS HURT, HE TOOK HIM TO THE NEAREST TOWN, AND PAID THE PEOPLE THERE TO CARE FOR HIM.'

SO, WHICH OF THE THREE DO YOU THINK WAS THE INJURED MAN'S NEIGHBOUR?

THE ONE WHO HAD MERCY ON HIM.

GO AND DO LIKEWISE.

46

GIVE US A *SIGN*, JESUS. GIVE US A SIGN FROM *HEAVEN*. SHOW US WHAT YOU CAN DO.

A *SIGN*?

YOU KNOW THAT RED SKY AT NIGHT MEANS GOOD WEATHER, AND YOU KNOW RED SKY IN THE MORNING MEANS BAD WEATHER.

YOU KNOW HOW TO INTERPRET THE APPEARANCE OF THE *SKY* BUT YOU CAN'T INTERPRET THE SIGNS OF THE TIMES YOU LIVE IN.

THE PEOPLE OF TODAY ARE EVIL AND GODLESS. YOU ASK FOR A *MIRACLE*? THE ONLY MIRACLE YOU WILL BE GIVEN IS THE ONE GIVEN TO *JONAH*. HE WAS IN THE BELLY OF THE WHALE THREE DAYS AND EMERGED ALIVE.

BE CAREFUL OF THE PHARISEES AND SADDUCEES, PETER.

BEWARE OF THEIR TEACHINGS.

TELL ME, WHO DO THE PEOPLE SAY THE SON OF MAN IS?

SOME SAY JOHN THE BAPTIST, THAT HE ESCAPED FROM HEROD.

OTHERS SAY *JEREMIAH*.

OR *ELIJAH*, OR AT THE VERY LEAST ONE OF THE *PROPHETS*, RETURNED TO US.

BUT WHO DO *YOU* SAY I AM?

YOU ARE THE *MESSIAH*, SON OF THE LIVING GOD.

BLESSED ARE YOU, PETER, FOR THIS WAS NOT TAUGHT TO YOU BY *MEN*, BUT BY MY FATHER IN HEAVEN.

YOU WILL BE A ROCK - A ROCK ON WHICH I WILL BUILD MY *CHURCH*. NOT EVEN THE GATES OF *HELL* WILL OVERCOME IT.

I WILL GIVE YOU THE KEYS TO THE KINGDOM OF HEAVEN.

YOU MUST NOT TELL ANYONE WHO I REALLY AM. THERE ARE TERRIBLE TIMES AHEAD. I WILL SUFFER MANY THINGS AT THE HANDS OF THE ELDERS AND CHIEF PRIESTS IN JERUSALEM. I MUST DIE BUT ON THE THIRD DAY I WILL BE RAISED BACK TO LIFE.

NEVER, LORD! THIS CAN'T HAPPEN TO *YOU*.

WE'LL *STOP* THEM SOMEHOW, WE'LL FIND A WAY TO -

ENOUGH!

SUCH TALK IS NOT FROM GOD, BUT THE *DEVIL*!

ANYONE WHO WANTS TO COME WITH ME, MUST FORGET HIS OWN LIFE, TAKE UP HIS *CROSS* AND FOLLOW *ME*.

WHOEVER WANTS TO SAVE HIS OWN LIFE, WILL *SURELY* LOSE IT. BUT WHOEVER LOSES HIS LIFE FOR *MY* SAKE, WILL FIND IT.

WHAT GOOD IS IT IF A MAN WINS THE WHOLE *WORLD*, BUT FORFEITS HIS SOUL?

THE SON OF MAN IS ABOUT TO ENTER HIS FATHER'S GLORY. SOME OF YOU STANDING HERE WILL NOT *DIE* BEFORE SEEING THE COMING OF THE KINGDOM OF GOD.

SOME DAYS LATER, JESUS TOOK PETER, JAMES AND JOHN, AND LED THEM UP A NEARBY MOUNTAIN.

ON THE SUMMIT, JESUS BEGAN TO PRAY.

HIS THREE COMPANIONS, EXHAUSTED BY THE CLIMB, HAD OTHER IDEAS.

BUT AS JESUS PRAYED, AN INCREDIBLE **CHANGE** CAME OVER HIM... ONE THE DISCIPLES COULDN'T HELP BUT NOTICE.

... MASTER ?

JESUS STOOD BEFORE THEM, HIS FACE SHINING LIKE THE **SUN**, HIS CLOTHES AS BRIGHT AS DAYLIGHT! IT HURT THEIR EYES EVEN TO **LOOK** AT HIM.

ON ONE SIDE OF JESUS STOOD MOSES AND ON THE OTHER THE PROPHET ELIJAH.

THE THREE FIGURES TALKED ABOUT THE WAY THAT GOD WOULD SOON FULFIL HIS PLAN, THROUGH JESUS' DEATH IN JERUSALEM.

MASTER ! WHAT CAN I DO ? LET ME MAKE THREE SHELTERS, ONE FOR EACH OF YOU !

PETER DIDN'T KNOW WHAT HE WAS SAYING, HE WAS SO OVERCOME WITH SHEER WONDER.

JUST THEN A CLOUD COVERED THE MOUNTAIN, AND A VOICE CAME FROM IT, SAYING:

THIS IS MY **SON** WHOM I LOVE. **LISTEN** TO HIM !

THE DISCIPLES FOLLOWED JESUS BACK DOWN THE MOUNTAIN IN SILENCE.

THEY HAD WITNESSED SOMETHING OF SUCH **ENORMITY**, THAT IT WOULD BE A LONG WHILE BEFORE THEY COULD FIND THE WORDS TO EVEN **BEGIN** TO DESCRIBE IT.

MARY AND MARTHA WERE TWO SISTERS WHO LIVED IN THE TOWN OF BETHANY.

THEIR BROTHER LAZARUS, A CLOSE FRIEND OF JESUS, BECAME CRITICALLY ILL.

THEY SENT WORD TO JESUS. BUT NO REPLY CAME, AND LAZARUS DIED.

PETER, TELL THE OTHERS WE'RE GOING TO BETHANY.

BETHANY? WE WERE DRIVEN OUT OF THERE WITH STONES LAST TIME. ARE YOU SURE?

OUR FRIEND LAZARUS HAS FALLEN ASLEEP, BUT I'M GOING THERE TO WAKE HIM UP SO THAT YOU MAY SEE THE POWER OF GOD.

BUT MASTER, IF HE'S UNWELL THE REST WILL DO HIM GOOD. ISN'T IT BETTER TO LET HIM SLEEP?

I WASN'T SPEAKING LITERALLY, PETER.

HE'S DEAD.

MARTHA—

OH LORD, IF ONLY YOU'D GOT HERE SOONER, YOU'RE A BUSY MAN I KNOW, AND WE ARE GRATEFUL, BUT—

MARTHA—

HE HUNG ON TO THE LAST. I TOLD HIM YOU'D COME, BUT HE JUST COULDN'T WAIT...

MARTHA!

OH I KNOW THAT. ON THE LAST DAY ALL THE DEAD WILL RISE AGAIN.

YOUR BROTHER WILL RISE AGAIN.

I AM THE RESURRECTION, AND THE LIFE. WHOEVER BELIEVES IN ME WILL LIVE EVEN THOUGH THEY DIE.

DO YOU BELIEVE THIS, MARTHA?

YES, LORD— YOU ARE THE CHRIST, THE SON OF GOD.

MARY! THE TEACHER IS HERE, AND IS ASKING FOR YOU.

AND SLOWLY...

FROM THE MURKY DARKNESS OF THE TOMB...

THE DEAD MAN APPEARED.

YOU WERE *DEAD*, BROTHER.

WHAT HAPPENED?

DEAD? AND NOW I AM ALIVE?!

WHAT TRICKERY IS THIS?

BUT I SAW IT MYSELF. THE MAN WAS DEAD AND BURIED!

TAKE OFF HIS GRAVE CLOTHES AND SET HIM FREE!

WE CAN'T LET HIM CONTINUE LIKE THIS. AT THIS RATE THE WHOLE NATION WILL FOLLOW HIM, NOT *US*. WE MUST HANG ON TO WHAT LITTLE POWER THE ROMANS HAVE LEFT US.

JESUS MUST BE STOPPED. AND *SOON*.

52

THE RAISING OF LAZARUS LED MANY JEWS TO PUT THEIR FAITH IN JESUS. FROM THAT MOMENT ON, THE CHIEF PRIESTS IN JERUSALEM MADE PLANS TO HAVE JESUS KILLED.

ALTHOUGH JESUS KNEW ALL OF THIS, HE LED HIS DISCIPLES TO THE CITY OF *JERUSALEM.*

IT WAS THE TIME OF THE PASSOVER.

AND NOT JUST JESUS, BUT LAZARUS TOO — A WALKING REMINDER OF JESUS' POWER.

YOU TWO, GO TO THE VILLAGE AHEAD. YOU'LL FIND A DONKEY THERE THAT HAS NEVER BEEN RIDDEN. BRING HIM TO ME.

AND SO THE DISCIPLES DID AS HE SAID, TELLING THE OWNER, 'THE MASTER NEEDS HIM,' JUST AS JESUS HAD TOLD THEM.

CENTURIES BEFORE, THE PROPHET ZECHARIAH HAD FORETOLD THESE EVENTS:

'REJOICE, YOU PEOPLE OF JERUSALEM.

'LOOK, YOUR KING HAS COME TO YOU! HE COMES VICTORIOUS, BUT ALSO HUMBLE, RIDING A YOUNG DONKEY.

'HE WILL MAKE *PEACE* BETWEEN THE NATIONS AND RULE FROM SEA TO SEA TO THE ENDS OF THE EARTH.'

THE GREAT CROWD THAT HAD COME TO JERUSALEM FOR THE PASSOVER HEARD THAT JESUS WAS COMING. AS HE ENTERED THE CITY, SHOUTS AND CHEERS FILLED THE AIR: '*HOSANNA! THE PROMISED KING HAS COME!* BLESSED IS HE WHO COMES IN THE NAME OF THE LORD.'

PEOPLE TOOK OFF THEIR CLOAKS AND LAID THEM IN JESUS' PATH. OTHERS LAID PALM LEAVES ON THE GROUND IN FRONT OF HIM.

IT WAS AS IF KING DAVID HIMSELF HAD RETURNED, TO RESTORE ISRAEL TO ITS FORMER GLORY.

HE'S A SCRAWNY THING, I'LL GIVE YOU TEN FOR HIM.

TEN? YOU *INSULT* ME! FIFTEEN, OR NOTHING!

FIFTEEN? ARE YOU *MAD*? WE'LL PAY NO MORE THAN ELEVEN, AND THAT'S GENEROUS.

I NEED TO BORROW MORE MONEY.

THE INTEREST WILL GO UP, YOU KNOW.

WITH ALMOST EVERY PAIR OF EYES AND EARS IN JERUSALEM WAITING TO SEE WHAT HE WOULD DO NEXT, JESUS WENT STRAIGHT TO THE TEMPLE'S OUTER COURT.

MY HOUSE SHOULD BE A HOUSE OF PRAYER FOR ALL NATIONS...

BUT YOU HAVE MADE IT INTO A DEN OF THIEVES!

JESUS THREW OUT ALL THE MONEY-CHANGERS AND STALL-HOLDERS — TO THE HORROR OF THE PRIESTS, WHO THRIVED ON THE TRADE.

DO YOU HEAR THE *NOISE* OUTSIDE? THERE ARE *CHILDREN* SHOUTING '*HOSANNA TO THE SON OF DAVID*.'

FROM THE MOUTHS OF CHILDREN, GOD RECEIVES PRAISE.

THAT'S IT! HE'S GONE TOO FAR THIS TIME!

I DON'T KNOW. JUST *WHO* DOES HE THINK HE IS? ENOUGH IS ENOUGH!

THE HOUR HAS COME FOR THE SON OF MAN TO BE GLORIFIED.

UNLESS AN EAR OF WHEAT FALLS TO THE GROUND AND DIES, IT REMAINS JUST A SINGLE SEED. BUT IF IT DIES, IT PRODUCES MANY SEEDS.

DO NOT LET YOURSELVES BE TROUBLED. I AM GOING ON AHEAD OF YOU TO PREPARE A PLACE FOR YOU. IN MY FATHER'S HOUSE THERE ARE MANY ROOMS.

I AM THE WAY, THE TRUTH AND THE LIFE. NO ONE COMES TO THE FATHER, EXCEPT THROUGH ME. IF YOU LOVE ME, YOU WILL DO WHAT I ASK OF YOU AND I WILL ASK THE FATHER TO SEND YOU A GUIDE WHO WILL BE WITH YOU *FOR EVER* - THE SPIRIT OF TRUTH.

I WILL BE GOING AWAY SOON. THE WORLD MUST SEE THAT I LOVE THE FATHER, AND THAT I WILL DO EXACTLY WHAT MY FATHER ASKS OF ME.

WHILE JESUS WAS SPEAKING ONE OF THE DISCIPLES SNEAKED AWAY...

JUDAS ISCARIOT RAN AS FAST AS HE COULD TO THE CHIEF PRIEST.

SO YOU'VE COME TO YOUR *SENSES* THEN. ARE YOU PREPARED TO TELL US WHERE WE CAN *FIND* HIM ?

I WILL. BUT THIS INFORMATION HAS A PRICE.

BUT OF COURSE.

THIRTY PIECES OF SILVER SHOULD BE ENOUGH, I'D SAY. *ENJOY* IT - YOU'VE *EARNED* IT.

BUT THE MONEY WAS TO BRING JUDAS NO PLEASURE. NO PLEASURE AT ALL.

IT WAS JUST BEFORE THE **PASSOVER** FEAST.

JESUS KNEW HIS TIME ON EARTH WAS COMING TO AN END AND THAT HE WOULD SOON RETURN TO HIS FATHER.

IT WAS NOW TIME FOR HIM TO **SHOW** HIS DISCIPLES JUST HOW MUCH HE LOVED THEM.

YOU KNOW THE COMMANDMENTS GIVEN TO MOSES. TODAY I GIVE YOU A **NEW** COMMANDMENT: LOVE ONE ANOTHER AS **I** HAVE LOVED **YOU**. EVERYONE WILL KNOW THAT YOU ARE MY DISCIPLES IF YOU LOVE ONE ANOTHER.

TAKE OFF YOUR SANDALS, AND **WATCH**.

LORD, PLEASE **DON'T** DO THIS! THERE'S NO **NEED**!

PETER, YOU DON'T SEE IT NOW, BUT LATER YOU WILL UNDERSTAND.

UNLESS YOU ALLOW ME TO WASH YOUR FEET, YOU CAN NO LONGER BE MY DISCIPLE.

LORD, IN **THAT** CASE, WASH MY HANDS AND HEAD AS WELL!

YOU ARE ALREADY **CLEAN**.

YOU CALL ME 'TEACHER' AND 'LORD', BUT I HAVE WASHED **YOUR** FEET. IN THE SAME WAY YOU SHOULD WASH EACH **OTHER'S**. I HAVE SET YOU AN EXAMPLE. IT'S ONE YOU SHOULD ALL FOLLOW.

NOW THAT YOU KNOW THESE THINGS, YOU WILL BE BLESSED IF YOU DO THEM.

THIS BREAD — TAKE AND EAT; THIS IS MY BODY, GIVEN FOR YOU. DO THIS IN REMEMBRANCE OF ME.

TAKE THIS CUP — DRINK FROM IT, ALL OF YOU. THIS IS MY BLOOD, POURED OUT FOR MANY FOR THE FORGIVENESS OF SINS.

'I TELL YOU THE TRUTH — I WILL NOT DRINK THE FRUIT OF THE VINE AGAIN, UNTIL THE KINGDOM OF GOD COMES.'

WHEN THEY HAD FINISHED THEIR MEAL, JESUS AND HIS DISCIPLES WENT OUTSIDE THE CITY WALLS — TO THE MOUNT OF OLIVES — TO PRAY.

SOON YOU WILL ALL RUN AWAY AND LEAVE ME.

IT WAS PROPHESIED, 'GOD WILL KILL THE SHEPHERD, AND THE SHEEP WILL SCATTER.'

NO, LORD! I WON'T LEAVE YOU.

PETER, BEFORE THE COCK CROWS TOMORROW MORNING, YOU WILL DISOWN ME *THREE* TIMES.

NEVER!

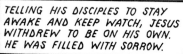

TELLING HIS DISCIPLES TO STAY AWAKE AND KEEP WATCH, JESUS WITHDREW TO BE ON HIS OWN. HE WAS FILLED WITH SORROW.

FATHER, I KNOW THAT *EVERYTHING* IS POSSIBLE FOR YOU.

PLEASE, TAKE THIS CUP OF SUFFERING AWAY FROM ME.

YET, NOT WHAT *I* WANT, BUT *YOUR* WILL BE DONE.

ARE YOU ALWAYS SLEEPING? COULDN'T YOU KEEP WATCH FOR ONE HOUR?

IT'S TOO LATE NOW. THE HOUR IS HERE.

OH! WE WERE, ER... JUST ERM...

LOOK. THE SON OF MAN IS BETRAYED INTO THE HANDS OF SINNERS. AND HERE COMES MY BETRAYER.

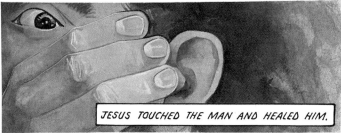

JESUS TOUCHED THE MAN AND HEALED HIM.

60

62

JESUS WAS LED AWAY TO SPEND THE REST OF THE NIGHT IN THE HANDS OF THE TEMPLE GUARDS.

BLASPHEMER!

PROPHESY *NOW*, 'MESSIAH'!

IF YOU'RE A *PROPHET*, TELL US WHO JUST *KICKED* YOU!

AT DAYBREAK, JESUS WAS TAKEN TO THE SEAT OF *REAL* POWER IN ISRAEL...

THE PALACE OF THE ROMAN GOVERNOR, PONTIUS PILATE.

THIS MAN IS GUILTY OF SUBVERTING THE WHOLE *NATION*. HE CLAIMS TO BE KING OF THE JEWS.

I SEE. AND *ARE* YOU? *ARE* YOU THEIR KING?

YOU SAY THAT I AM A KING, BUT MY KINGDOM IS NOT FROM THIS WORLD.

LOOK PILATE, IF HE WERE NOT A CRIMINAL, THEN WE WOULDN'T BE WASTING YOUR TIME.

BUT PILATE COULD FIND NOTHING WRONG WITH HIM.

SO PILATE DECIDED TO LET THE PEOPLE CHOOSE JESUS' FATE. IT WAS A PASSOVER CUSTOM TO RELEASE A CONDEMNED PRISONER.

THE CROWD COULD CHOOSE BETWEEN JESUS OR *BARABBAS* — A MAN CHARGED WITH MURDER FOR HIS PART IN AN UPRISING AGAINST THE ROMANS

WHO WOULD YOU HAVE ME RELEASE? *BARABBAS*? OR THIS MAN HERE, WHO CLAIMS TO BE YOUR *KING*?

BARABBAS!

BUT WHY? WHAT CRIME HAS HE COMMITTED?

WHAT WOULD YOU HAVE ME *DO* WITH HIM?

CRUCIFY HIM!

CRUCIFY HIM!

CRUCIFY HIM!

CRUCIFY HIM!

CRUCIFY HIM!

THEN I SHALL RELEASE BARABBAS.

I AM INNOCENT OF THIS MAN'S BLOOD. HE IS *YOUR* RESPONSIBILITY.

HAVE HIM FLOGGED AND *CRUCIFY* HIM!

YESSIR.

I HAVE *SINNED*! I HAVE BETRAYED AN INNOCENT MAN! TAKE YOUR MONEY BACK!

BUT *JUDAS*, THAT'S NO CONCERN OF *OURS*. YOU CAME TO *US*, REMEMBER? NO, THE MONEY IS *YOURS*.

JUDAS NEVER LIVED TO ENJOY THE MONEY. HURLING THE THIRTY PIECES OF SILVER INTO THE TEMPLE, HE LEFT THE CITY AND HANGED HIMSELF.

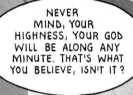

WHIPPED, BEATEN, BLEEDING AND COVERED IN SPIT, THE HEIR TO THE THRONE OF DAVID WAS FINALLY CROWNED *KING*. THEN THEY LED HIM AWAY TO CRUCIFY HIM.

CRUCIFY HIM!
CRUCIFY HIM!

CRUCIFY HIM!
CRUCIFY HIM!

CRUCIFY HIM!
CRUCIFY HIM!

THOSE CONDEMNED TO BE CRUCIFIED WERE FORCED TO CARRY THEIR OWN CROSS TO THE PLACE OF CRUCIFIXION.

ALREADY WEAKENED BY BEATINGS, FLOGGINGS AND TORTURE, JESUS COULD SCARCELY **WALK**, LET ALONE CARRY HIS CROSS.

LOOK AT HIM. HE'S GOING TO **DROP** IT!

GO ON, **PICK IT UP**!

TOO **HEAVY** IS IT, YOUR MAJESTY? HA! THAT'S ROYALTY FOR YOU!

A MAN CALLED SIMON, FROM CYRENE IN NORTH AFRICA, WAS IN THE CROWD. AS JESUS WAS TOO WEAK TO CARRY THE CROSS, THE SOLDIERS FORCED SIMON TO CARRY IT INSTEAD.

IN THIS WAY, WITH SIMON CARRYING THE CROSS AND JESUS STUMBLING ALONGSIDE HIM, THEY MADE THEIR WAY THROUGH THE STREETS UP THE HILL CALLED **GOLGOTHA** – THE PLACE OF THE SKULL.

66

AND THEY CRUCIFIED HIM.

HERE IS JESUS—
KING OF THE JEWS

AS THE LIGHT OF THE WORLD WAS EXTINGUISHED, SO A GREAT DARKNESS FELL OVER THE LAND, SUCH AS HAD NOT BEEN SEEN ON EARTH SINCE CREATION BEGAN.

JOSEPH OF ARIMATHEA, A MEMBER OF THE HIGH COUNCIL, WHO HAD SPOKEN ON JESUS' BEHALF, GAVE HIM HIS OWN TOMB, SAVING JESUS FROM THE MASS GRAVE RESERVED FOR CRIMINALS.

AT SUNRISE ON THE **THIRD** DAY, MARY MAGDALENE, AND MARY, JAMES' MOTHER, WENT TO THE TOMB WHERE JESUS' BODY HAD BEEN LAID.

THE **STONE**— IT'S BEEN **MOVED**!

DO THEY HATE HIM SO MUCH THAT THEY WOULD EVEN DESECRATE HIS **GRAVE**?

WAIT! ONE OF THEM IS STILL HERE!

BE CAREFUL!

DO NOT BE AFRAID.

YOU ARE LOOKING FOR **JESUS**, WHO WAS CRUCIFIED. HE IS NOT HERE, BUT HAS **RISEN**, AS HE SAID HE WOULD.

GO, TELL HIS DISCIPLES HE IS **ALIVE** AND WILL MEET THEM IN GALILEE.

WHAT'S HAPPENED?

THEY'RE RIGHT, HIS BODY IS GONE.

WHAT CAN IT MEAN?

OH JESUS, WHAT HAVE THEY **DONE** TO YOU?

...MARY?

MARY, WHY DO YOU LOOK FOR THE **LIVING** AMONG THE **DEAD**?

TEACHER!!

HE HAD BEEN **DEAD**. THAT WAS WITHOUT QUESTION. SHE HAD **BEEN** THERE AS HE DIED, AND YET HERE HE WAS – ALIVE! **ALIVE!**

MARY RAN AS FAST AS SHE COULD TO TELL THE OTHERS THE **INCREDIBLE** NEWS. **JESUS WAS ALIVE!!**

DO NOT HOLD ON TO ME, FOR I HAVE NOT YET RETURNED TO MY FATHER.

GO AND TELL THE OTHERS, 'I AM RETURNING TO MY FATHER, WHO IS ALSO **YOUR** FATHER; TO MY GOD AND **YOUR** GOD.'

BUT WHEN THEY HEARD HER SAY THAT JESUS WAS ALIVE AND SHE HAD SEEN HIM THEY DID NOT BELIEVE HER.

WHICH IS WHEN **JESUS** SHOWED UP, IN **PERSON**:

PEACE BE WITH YOU. WHY ARE YOU FRIGHTENED? I **TOLD** YOU WHAT WOULD HAPPEN – THE MESSIAH WOULD BE PUT TO **DEATH**, AND ON THE THIRD DAY RISE **AGAIN**.

WELL DON'T JUST **STAND** THERE. I'D LIKE SOMETHING TO **EAT**!

ALL THE REMAINING DISCIPLES WERE THERE AND **SAW** HIM THAT DAY.

ALL EXCEPT FOR **THOMAS**, THAT IS...

GREETINGS.

AARGGHH!! IT'S A **GHOST**!!!

WELL, **I** DON'T BELIEVE IT.

HE'S **DEAD**, WE ALL **SAW** HIM DIE, AND UNLESS I SEE THE HOLES IN HIS HANDS FOR **MYSELF**, I WON'T BELIEVE A **WORD** OF IT!

THOMAS..!

HERE, FEEL MY HANDS, FEEL THE **HOLES**. FEEL THE SPEAR WOUND IN MY SIDE.

MY **LORD**! MY LORD AND **GOD**!

YOU BELIEVE BECAUSE YOU CAN **SEE** ME. HOW MUCH MORE BLESSED ARE THOSE WHO BELIEVE WITHOUT **EVER** SEEING ME!

JESUS APPEARED TO THE DISCIPLES SEVERAL TIMES OVER THE FOLLOWING DAYS AND WEEKS.

BUT AN ERA HAD COME TO AN END, AND NO ONE SEEMED CERTAIN OF WHAT WOULD HAPPEN NEXT. THIS IN MIND, PETER THOUGHT IT TIME HE PICKED UP HIS LIFE AGAIN.

SO ONE NIGHT PETER AND THE DISCIPLES SET OUT IN THE BOAT TO CATCH FISH — BUT WHEN THE SUN CAME UP, THEIR NETS WERE STILL EMPTY... A FIGURE ON THE SHORE CALLED TO THEM.

FRIENDS, HAVE YOU CAUGHT MANY FISH?

NONE! IT'S AS IF THE SEA IS EMPTY!

THEN WHY NOT CAST YOUR NETS OUT OVER THE *RIGHT*-HAND SIDE OF THE BOAT? YOU'LL FIND SOME THERE.

TOO TIRED TO ARGUE, THE DISCIPLES DID AS THE MAN SAID. AT ONCE THE NETS BECAME SO FULL OF FISH THAT THEY WERE UNABLE TO HAUL THEM ABOARD.

WHO IS THAT MAN?!

IT'S THE *LORD*! LOOK! IT'S *HIM*!

LORD!

PETER, GO BACK AND GET SOME OF THOSE FISH. I'M PREPARING *BREAKFAST* FOR YOU.

EVERYTHING THE PROPHETS SAID WAS *TRUE*: 'THE MESSIAH WILL *DIE*, AND ON THE THIRD DAY RISE FROM THE DEAD.

'IN *HIS* NAME, FORGIVENESS FOR SINS WILL BE PREACHED TO *ALL* THE NATIONS ON EARTH, STARTING IN JERUSALEM.'

PETER, DO YOU LOVE ME?

LORD, YOU *KNOW* I DO. YOU KNOW EVERYTHING.

THEN TAKE CARE OF MY SHEEP FOR ME.

JESUS ASKED PETER THIS QUESTION THREE TIMES. IN THIS WAY JESUS SHOWED PETER HE FORGAVE HIM FOR HIS TRIPLE DENIAL.

PETER'S DAYS AS A FISHERMAN WERE OVER. HE NOW HAD A NEW JOB...

ALL AUTHORITY IN HEAVEN AND EARTH HAS BEEN GIVEN TO *ME.*

GO INTO THE WORLD AND MAKE DISCIPLES FROM ALL NATIONS, BAPTIZING THEM IN THE NAME OF THE FATHER, THE SON, AND THE HOLY SPIRIT.

I AM GOING TO SEND THE ONE MY *FATHER* PROMISED YOU — *THE HOLY SPIRIT.* DO NOT LEAVE JERUSALEM, BUT *WAIT* FOR HIM THERE.

YOU WILL RECEIVE *POWER* WHEN THE HOLY SPIRIT COMES, AND YOU WILL BE MY WITNESSES IN JERUSALEM, JUDEA, AND TO THE ENDS OF THE EARTH! YOUR WORK IS ONLY *BEGINNING!*

AND AS HE STOOD THERE BLESSING THEM, HE WAS TAKEN *UP,* BEFORE THEIR EYES...

JUST THEN TWO ANGELS APPEARED SAYING, 'MEN OF GALILEE, WHY ARE YOU LOOKING AT THE SKY? JESUS HAS BEEN TAKEN FROM YOU INTO *HEAVEN,* AND IN THE SAME WAY HE WILL *RETURN* TO YOU.'